ROLAND SHARP, COUNTRY DOCTOR:

MEMORIES OF A LIFE WELL LIVED

Roland P. Sharp, at age 67, during the year the osteopathic medical school
in Lewisburg, WV, enrolled its first students.

ROLAND SHARP, COUNTRY DOCTOR:

MEMORIES OF A LIFE WELL LIVED

WITH

SOME THOUGHTS ABOUT MEDICINE

Pocahontas Communications Cooperative
Dunmore WV 24934
2008

Second Printing 2009, McClain Printing Company, Parsons, WV

Photographs courtesy of Roland P. Sharp, unless otherwise noted.

Library of Congress Cataloging-in-Publication-Data
Sharp, Roland P. 1907 -
Roland Sharp, Country Doctor: Memories of a Life Well Lived

ISBN – 0-87012-771-3
Library of Congress Control Number - 2008920744

1. Rural Medicine; 2. Biography; 3. Osteopathy

ROLAND SHARP COUNTRY DOCTOR may be ordered directly from:

Pocahontas Communications Cooperative, Dunmore WV 24934

$25 plus $2 per copy for shipping and handling. WV residents add $1.50 for sales tax.

Or you can order ROLAND SHARP COUNTRY DOCTOR and other items celebrating to the history and culture of the Allegheny Mountains online – go to www.alleghenymountainradio.org and click on "AMR Store."

ROLAND SHARP
Country Doctor

Table of Contents

Introduction

About seven years ago we at Pocahontas Communications Cooperative started thinking about doing an audio autobiography of one of our area's most beloved and accomplished citizens, Dr. Roland Paul Sharp, who had recently retired from the practice of medicine at the age of ninety four. Dr. Sharp has had a fascinating life. Born in 1907 on a small farm in Frost, West Virginia, he later taught in one-room schools for more than a decade while attending college part-time. After receiving his college degree at the age of twenty eight, he began to work toward becoming a medical doctor, a goal he achieved when he was thirty five. Dr. Sharp then practiced for seventeen years as a coal company doctor in southern West Virginia, serving miners and their families and delivering over 1,500 babies—often in a cabin up a hollow or over a mountain and once, with forceps, in the dark! At age fifty four he returned to his home county of Pocahontas and worked as a rural general practitioner for another four decades.

During part of that time he was deeply involved in medical education, serving as the founding president of the West Virginia School of Osteopathic Medicine [WVSOM] and setting that school on a course that emphasized the holistic and compassionate approach to practicing medicine that characterized his own life's work. In 2007, in his hundredth year, WVSOM earned the distinction of having the largest percentage of graduates practicing medicine in rural areas of any medical school in the world—carrying through on another goal set by Dr. Sharp and his fellow founders of the college.

Dr. Sharp has received numerous awards over the years. The West Virginia Society of Osteopathic Medicine has conferred several honors on him: in 1971, Practitioner of the Year; in 1976, the Distinguished Service Certificate, the highest honor conferred by the society and the first awarded since 1955. In 1979 the National Student Osteopathic Medical Association honored

Dr. Sharp as Outstanding Medical Educator in the United States. In 1989 WVSOM and the West Virginia Board of Regents authorized granting a Doctor of Science, *honoris causae,* to Dr. Sharp—a rare honor in the history of the state. In 2006 his alma mater, Concord University, awarded him an honorary Doctor of Humanitarian Service degree. In 2007 Dr. Sharp received a Rotary Distinguished Service Award for his commitment to rural health care and his fifty eight years of service to the Marlinton Rotary Club. On the occasion of his hundredth birthday in December 2007, Governor Joe Manchin III recognized Dr. Sharp's service to rural medicine in the region with a Distinguished West Virginian Award. Dr. Sharp has been listed in *Who's Who in North America* and in *American Men and Women of Science.*

As a man, a physician, and an educator, Roland Sharp exemplifies the best of Pocahontas County and its way of life. Respected by all and beloved by his patients and neighbors, his is a life well worth celebrating. We hope to honor him by publication of this book, told mainly in his own words, and to share his story with his neighbors, Pocahontas County generations yet to come, and the rest of the country. Not only does it offer a glimpse back into rural America three generations ago, but it also portrays a life well lived. In addition, we hope people concerned with the future of health care in America will heed his words about the core values that should guide the practice of medicine.

Over the course of several years different people have worked on the project from time to time. Thanks to LeAnna Alderman, Sarah Burt-Kinderman Riley, Amy Henry, and Wendy Campbell, who conducted interviews. Sarah, Wendy and Sue Shears did the transcribing. LeAnna, Sarah, Wendy, Kama Wagner, Dr. Sharp's granddaughter Paula Sharp Jones, and I worked on editing this book. Bill McNeel and Ken Sullivan gave the manuscript a final going over prior to publication. Thanks to Paula Jones, Dr. Olen Jones, and Dr. John Sharp for their tributes to Dr. Roland and to Julian Rittenhouse for permission to reproduce the lyrics of his song. Photographs were supplied by Dr. Roland Sharp, Jack Feller, the West Virginia School of Osteopathic Medicine, and the Kirksville College of Osteopathic Medicine of A.T. Still University, as well as the National Archives and the Eastern Regional Coal Archives at Craft Memorial Library, Bluefield, West Virginia. Mindy Bond provided extensive help in scanning and designing the photo presentations and whipping the book into final shape. Credit for book design is due to Wendy Campbell, Colleen Anderson, and Mindy Bond. We're grateful to Michelle McKinnie and the staff at McClain Printing for their continuing fine work in printing and promoting our publications. We also appreciate Barbara McCarty's help in locating photographs and working with Dr. Sharp to review drafts of the manuscript, as well as the contributions of the many people who spoke with us about Dr. Sharp's life and career.

Most of all I thank Dr. Roland Sharp, still active and insightful at the age of one hundred, for reviewing earlier drafts and for permitting us to share his story with you. Any errors are ours alone.

Gibbs Kinderman
Pocahontas Communications Cooperative
Dunmore, WV 24934
July 2008

The Pocahontas Communications Cooperative operates Allegheny Mountain Radio, a noncommercial radio mini-network that provides the only local radio service to an isolated rural area in the mountains along the Virginia–West Virginia border. Part of the Cooperative's mission is to celebrate and preserve the history and culture of our area. In addition to oral history programming and live traditional music on the radio, we have produced several CDs of local music and published books on regional literature and history.

Dr. Sharp was born in Frost, Pocahontas County, WV.
Maps show key locations in his story.

Childhood in the Country

1907–1921

"You don't dig yourself out of poverty.
You educate yourself out of poverty."
—Roland Sharp's father Aaron

I was born on December 30th, 1907, the son of Aaron and Odessa Jordan Sharp. I grew up on a farm right across the hill from Frost in Pocahontas County, West Virginia. Frost was home to several families, a church, a parsonage, and one store. You had to buy all of your products from there, except for your winter clothes. It was a very quiet place then. My grandparents lived in Frost, but I lived on the original homestead, on the site settled by the first Sharp to cross the Alleghenies. That was John Sharp, Sr., who came here in the early 1800s when the first Presbyterian minister settled in Hillsboro, about 30 miles from Frost. John Sharp had a land grant or bought land that reached from Frost to Glade Hill. He also owned land on Thorny Creek and Buffalo Mountain near Green Bank. He apparently came here for land.

I lived on the original John Sharp farm until I was 19. My dad grew up in that same house. He lived in that house from the time he was about ten or eleven years old. He wasn't born in that house though. He was born in a log house there on the farm where his father also was born. The original cemetery still stands there today, a testament to generations of families who settled this land. Anyway, I lived there until I finished high school.

The Farm in Frost

What I remember most about growing up on the Sharp farm is that we had something like fifteen cows and maybe forty or fifty sheep. We had quite a large number of sheep because they were more profitable than cattle at the time. We cut a lot of hay, about twenty stacks, which was a considerable quantity at the time. Hay was not baled back then. It was put into stacks and we usually had the barns filled, with fifteen or twenty stacks left over. So each year my dad kept as many cows as he could feed with the year's bounty of hay.

As far as I know, my dad had the first purebred cattle in this district. Back during World War I, he went to Ohio on the train. In Ohio, he bought a couple of registered short-horn cattle, a Delaine Merino ram, and two Duroc Jersey hogs, all purebreds. Dad had them shipped in here on the train. Those animals rode from Ohio to Clover Lick on the train! Well, Dad went down to Clover Lick and hauled the sheep and hogs home on a wagon and then drove the cattle home. I recall that he took one of the short-horn calves to the county fair a year later. He hauled it part of the way on the wagon and led it the rest of the way. It must have been a pretty good specimen because he won a second-place red ribbon. I remember that day well.

I also remember that we grew corn, oats, and wheat on the farm. We raised a lot of corn, about six or seven acres. We hoed, plowed, and planted it all by hand. Back then they considered a farmer lazy if he didn't keep his corn neatly plowed and hoed.

My dad usually grew two or three acres of wheat, five or six acres of oats, and about an acre of buckwheat. The buckwheat was grown for two things; buckwheat cakes for us in the winter, and fare for the birds [chickens] and the bees. Bees made honey from buckwheat bloom. The honey was very dark, almost blackened from the buckwheat. However, buckwheat ultimately inspired the bees to produce so much honey that all of the farmers felt that buckwheat was a good investment. We had seven hives of bees on the farm all of the time. Honey was one of the best sweeteners back then.

When everything was harvested on the farm in the fall, we took the buckwheat, some corn, and some wheat to Dunmore to a roller mill and had it ground. It took a whole day to haul a load from Frost to Dunmore, a distance of six miles. We came back with a barrel or two of flour, a sack or two of cornmeal, and some buckwheat flour. My dad also had wheat ground that we used for cereal. We looked over the wheat by hand to make sure it was properly cleaned before we made our cereal. Then my dad had the wheat ground so it looked and tasted like Wheatena. Wheatena looks like Cream of Wheat only it's the brownish color of wheat rather than white. That was really a welcome change from eating oatmeal every morning! We used it as cereal and we ate oatmeal and cornbread. Not a single one of us ever had rickets. After I grew up, I realized that our simple farm diet had been very good!

We had plenty of apples. There were three orchards on our farm at that time. We always made a barrel or two of cider. My dad allowed us to drink the cider when it was sweet, but as soon as it began to ferment he sealed up the barrel and let nature turn it into apple cider vinegar. That was our vinegar for the next year, with enough left over for the neighbors. You never had to buy vinegar.

After a few years, the mill we went to at Dunmore changed. When you arrived with your wheat, oats, corn, and buckwheat, they took your cereals or your grain raw and just gave you prepackaged cereal and grains in sacks or boxes. You didn't have to wait for it. They just measured what you brought and gave you the equivalent amount of milled product. You just unloaded yours and the miller measured your wheat. He knew exactly how much flour or cereal each bushel would make. If you took ten bushels in, you'd just load the equivalent in flour up and head back home. That made going to the mill much easier.

But what I was about to tell about was hoeing corn. That was the worst thing that my brother and I had to do! Well, planting corn was bad enough because it was so tedious to do by hand. But when it got hot in June and July, we had to hoe the corn and the weeds. We could hardly put up with that, and we'd groan and grumble.

My dad said something to me then that has always stuck with me. "You don't like hoeing this corn? Just remember this; you don't dig yourself out of poverty. You educate yourself out of poverty. So you hoe corn or go to school, whichever. That's your choice." So after I had hoed enough corn, I decided I would rather educate myself out of poverty.

There were lots of good times on the farm, though. It wasn't all tedious, hard work. Knapps Creek ran right through our farm and there were some fine swimming holes there. When my dad wasn't with us and we had neighbor boys helping hoe the corn, we would hoe to the end of the row near the creek bank and then take a swim for the next hour or two. And if we didn't expect my dad back, it was often longer than that! We kept an eye out for him and if we heard any noises or saw anything suspicious, we got out, put our clothes on in a hurry, and went back to hoeing.

All of the people around us were farmers. There was nothing but farmers in the area. The only thing I can remember other than farmers was a blacksmith and a carpenter. The blacksmith did all the horseshoeing and kept the wagons in shape. There were blacksmith shops at Frost, Huntersville, and Dunmore. There were a couple of blacksmiths in all of those places.

Not many farmers had money. What little stock they had they sold and that was the only money they had. They raised everything they ate. All they had to buy were their clothes, sugar, spices, salt, and coffee. That's all that I can think of that farmers had to buy. My parents usually sent away to Baltimore for boxes of dried prunes, dried peaches, and dried apricots. They came in wooden boxes in ten, twenty, forty or fifty pound quantities, and we ate them through the winter months.

Roland Sharp, right, age 13, at a farm on Knapps Creek south of Frost, circa 1922, with four of his five siblings: Georgie Lee, right front; Clarabelle, left front; Martha Lou, back, right of the girl with the hair bow, and Daniel Gordon, standing on left. Youngest brother, Richard, had not yet been born.

Today a family of two or three will use as much as five pounds of sugar in a week. The average family in the teens didn't use five pounds a month, even with a whole family of children. They sweetened a lot with maple syrup. Those that didn't have maple syrup grew some cane and used cane sorghum to sweeten their cereal. They sweetened most everything with syrup or sorghum, which is molasses made with the juice of the cane.

It seemed to me that everybody had plenty to eat at that time. There were really no obese persons and few who were undernourished. Those who lived on a farm gave food to those who did not live on a farm or to those they knew needed food. Everybody milked their own cows and shared milk with those who didn't own cows.

Everyone shared generously with those in need. To tell the truth, I didn't really know there was a depression until I was in college. But I think the hard times during the Depression have been overemphasized because, as far as I'm concerned, the Depression created a more concerned group of people, a more compassionate people; a more understanding people.

By Hand, Then Machine

Most of the equipment was hand equipment. In my earliest days, most of the hay was cut by hand with a scythe. All of the wheat, oats, and buckwheat were cut with a type of scythe called a cradle. My dad had the first horse-drawn grain binder in the whole community. I don't remember how early that was, but it must have been in the teens. It was definitely before World War I. I think it got the name binder because it made a sheaf of grain and tied it with twine, generating bundles of oats about a foot in diameter. Then my dad got a hay rake that was pulled by a horse. You still had to use your hands to pull the rake up. You'd rake up so much hay and then with a handle you'd pull the rake up, dump the hay out, and rake more.

My dad had sheep clippers that you would crank for clipping. He was also the first to have those. Before that you just sheared sheep with a pair of shears that were like the scissors you cut cloth with, just much larger and heavier. The clippers were an important improvement.

Horse-drawn mowing machines came in some time around then, I'd say, about 1910. I can't remember the first one. Even though there were horse-drawn mowing machines, most of the farmers didn't buy them, still preferring to cut their hay with a scythe. People were skeptical until they proved that something was going to be worth it. I can remember seeing people mow their fields, good-sized fields, with scythes. A couple of people could get out with a scythe and mow an acre of grass in a couple of hours. And that was considered great speed. Of course with the horse-drawn one you could probably cut three or four acres. It was so much better. They could really cut the grass.

The first people I can remember bringing threshing machines into this area were the Crummetts, who came over from Highland County in Virginia. The next people were the Gums, who came from Dunmore. They would start out in late August when the grain was harvested and dry. They would start at Dunmore and come right down the valley into Frost and right down Knapps Creek, probably all the way to Mr. Harper's. It would take maybe a month to do that, threshing all of the grain in the valley.

For a long time the threshing machines were powered by tractors that were fired with wood instead of coal. They ran the threshing machine with that steam-driven engine, but they had to put it thirty feet or something like that from the threshing machine or the engine would set everything on fire. The machines had a long, long belt. You've probably seen motors with belts, but those older belts were very long, to keep the fire away; plus they put screen over the stacks. Then when the machine got to threshing, they just took wood and a little bit of coal, and they would fire that motor just like they fire a train. If they started up at Dunmore, Mr. Ernest Moore was one of the first people, then some Buzzards next. This family would go with the thresher to the next farm, and then both of them would go to the next farm, until they got down the road far enough that the people below would come up. There was no exchange of money and the people who threshed just took so much grain, calling it a toll. By today's measures it was very, very minimal payment.

Dunmore, as the Railroad Approaches

The flour and grain mill was the main activity at Dunmore. In the earliest times it was run by water. There is an all-season spring above Dunmore that doesn't freeze over. That spring is supposed to be a medicinal spring. It ran in the ditch by the side of the highway. They called those ditches "millraces." That spring supplied the waterpower for the water wheel. The water ran in that millrace to Dunmore and powered the mill. Finally Mr. Sheets, who ran the mill, got a gasoline motor. I remember that's the first one I ever saw. It was a great big motor, really wide, with a big wheel on each side. To start it, you had to turn those wheels by hand. When it took off, that motor scared anybody who hadn't seen one before, because it shook the whole big building when it ran. That was a three-story building, too!

That mill was the main business. The highway went through Dunmore down by Pritchard's store. There were about three generations of Pritchards that ran the store at Dunmore and W. J. Pritchard ran another one in an old building that still stands at Frost. It had a porch on the outside that ran all the way across the front and around the side. The store run by W.J. Pritchard at Frost was similar to the one at Dunmore, except the one at Dunmore was a much larger store. It was run by the rest of the Pritchard family and you could buy most any type of clothing, hardware, and groceries at that store. They had a much larger supply and variety of things than the one at Frost.

That highway [State Route 92 today] was the main road through Dunmore. There was no other road. There was a store back on this side of the Methodist church. I can't remember who ran that store but Mr. Swecker was either in that store or beside it. Mr. Swecker was a cabinetmaker and a very good carpenter, but his main business was making caskets. About everybody from this area bought their caskets from Mr. Swecker at Dunmore.

In 1900 the Chesapeake and Ohio Railway reached Marlinton. People in Dunmore and Frost went to a station called Sitlington, which is four miles from Dunmore. People went there because there was just one hill between Dunmore and Sitlington. Coming out, you had to cross the Greenbrier River to get to the railroad. The railroad was on the west side or the other side of the river. You had to cross the river on our one-way iron bridge. When you came back on this side, you went up a little hill. Other than that hill, there wasn't any trouble with a team of horses getting a load of materials.

I can remember that if there was a big or heavy load, you would put half of it on the wagon and haul it up to the top of the hill, unload it, and then go back to the station and get the other half. When you got that half to the top of the hill, you would reload your first half. If you were lucky, someone else might be there at the same time and would hook his team of horses to your wagon tongue and pull you to the top of the hill—if you would do the same for him! People always cooperated like that.

Raywood was built later, beginning in 1914. It was just up the river, one mile from Sitlington, but it was on this side of the river, the east side. Raywood was strictly a lumber mill town. They had a double-band saw mill like the one at Cass. All you had to do to get there was to cross Sitlington Creek and follow on the south [east] side of the Greenbrier River.

A Brief Family History, as Complicated by the Civil War

My paternal grandfather Abraham Sharp served in the Union army for two or three years during the Civil War. He was the direct source of most of what I learned then about the Civil War. He told us lots of stories.

My maternal grandfather George Jordan was a Confederate, although he was too young to be in the service. With the stories of the two grandfathers, I got quite a diversity of ideas about the Civil War. My grandparents on my mother's side were Confederates who lived in Virginia and my father's family, Union sympathizers, lived here. So when I heard about General Sheridan from my Grandpa Sharp, he was a great man. But when he was mentioned to my grandmother [Lucy Horn Jordan]—well, she wouldn't allow you to even mention him! If you opened your mouth about General Sheridan, she would go into a real spasm. She lived in the Shenandoah Valley and basically Sheridan's cavalry was the one that defeated Lee there. He just kept Lee totally off balance there. I'm not sure whether it was his troops that captured her father, who was a Confederate, or whether General Sheridan was an accessory to the crime. She just prayed that heaven and earth would fall on that old skunk. That was just about as far as she could go. Don't mention him.

The people were divided here in Pocahontas County. Up in the flatwoods, which is where the Brethren Church is today, two Union believers, an Arbogast and I don't remember the other person, were killed by some of the local Confederate sympathizers. They called it bushwhacking. They were bushwhacked in that streak of woods that goes through just above the Rittenhouse farm. That farm was just wooded area at that time, back when the old road went through there [near today's state Route 92 a couple of miles north of Frost]. It went through a deep patch of woods. Two were killed there.

The Civil War caused a lot of division in the community for years. It resulted in the creation of two Methodist churches here at Frost. There was a Northern Methodist church in the village of Frost and a Southern Methodist church a mile below Frost. All the Confederate group went to that church. I never remember my grandmother being in the church at Frost.

Maternal grandfather, George Jordan, circa 1940.

My grandfather would go to either of those churches. He was not radical about either one. He was born in Albemarle County, Virginia and grew up and was educated in New Market. He was only five years old, I believe he said, when the Civil War began. He didn't have parents in the war. He didn't have that feeling my grandmother did. Her father was a prisoner for two years and she always claimed that that was the cause of his early death, starvation in a Union prison. However, she didn't consider how Union prisoners starved in southern prisons even more frequently, because the South actually didn't have food or at least didn't have the abundance of food and supplies that the Northerners had.

Most of the people on Knapps Creek here who were Methodist went to the Southern Methodist church and the people from Frost and above toward Dunmore came down and went to the Northern Methodist church. Those two merged in 1939. I don't think it was before that. Then in the 1968 the United Brethren and the Northern and Southern Methodist all went together and became the United Methodist.

Grandpa Gets a Medical License, and the Mail

My maternal grandfather was a Democrat. His name was George Jordan. They called him "Jerdan." He was a doctor and came to his medicine in 1895 and he was an old, old man. I probably shouldn't say this, but I've told people many, many times he was the only Democrat in this area who could read or write. I guess you could say my dad, his son in law, followed in his footsteps!

I think I should give you a little sample of how people used to become doctors. My grandfather was educated in New Market, Virginia, where he graduated from the Polytechnic Institute. After he graduated, he signed with Henkel brothers [The Henkel Press], one of the oldest publishers in Virginia, for a three-year preceptorship in printing. He became an excellent typesetter and publisher. The Henkel brothers sent him to the western mountains of Virginia, to a town called Monterey. In 1877 he established the Highland County *Recorder* newspaper that still exists today. He did such a good job at that they decided they would have a newspaper in Pendleton County [West Virginia], and thereafter he helped establish the *South Branch Times.* His first two children were born in Monterey. Then my mother and two of her sisters were born in Pendleton County. While he was in Pendleton in the town of Franklin President Grover Cleveland appointed him to the Government Printing Office in Washington.

While my grandfather was in Washington, he decided to study medicine. He worked in the printing office and went to medical lectures at several places, including Georgetown. Their [school] term lasted anywhere from three months to two years. They didn't have any laboratory or cadavers or anything. Actually all it involved was medical lectures until he was qualified or licensed in West Virginia. After Cleveland was defeated for a second term, my grandfather came back to Pendleton County and practiced a short time, five years. He then came to Pocahontas County in 1899 to look the place over, and he bought the house in Frost in 1900. He never studied with other doctors—just got his license, hung out his sign, and started practicing medicine!

Until World War I medicine was nothing but guesswork. You just comforted the patient, poulticed the patient, puked the patient, purged him, bled him, and sweated him. For example, they would use fumes from heated onions to get mucous loosened.

He passed a lot of what he knew on to my grandma. She was about as knowledgeable when a patient came in. And the two of them were ultra sanitary. You couldn't touch a knife or a fork until your hands had spent some time in the wash pan!

Grandpa didn't make enough money from doctoring to live, so he helped carry the mail to make extra money. My father contracted with the Post Office until the RFD [Rural Free Delivery] Amendment of 1914 or '15, when the government appointed rural mail carriers. Grandpa helped him out from time to time.

I was a little boy the first time I went down to Huntersville from our farm. I went with my grandfather Jordan. My grandfather was carrying the mail that day. My dad had the contract to carry the mail from Frost to Huntersville and back and he rode a horse or went in a buggy to carry out his duties. Although my dad had the formal contract, any day he didn't want to go, he could get almost anyone from the community to take over. All of the mail could be carried in one pocket of his saddlebags.

That day my grandpa went and we rode in the buggy. As far as I remember, we didn't pick up any letter or anything between Frost and Mrs. Pritchard's post office at Sunset. Mrs. Eudora Pritchard lived there. She was the postmistress. At Sunset he went in and picked up some letters. From Sunset there wasn't a single letter until Huntersville. We went to the post office there, where Mr. Joe Lowry was the postmaster. He fixed up a little batch of mail for us. You didn't have a mailbag. You just took it in your hand and stuck it in your saddlebag pocket. We got our lunch and ate it at Barlow's Store.

Huntersville would still be the county seat today, if the Chesapeake and Ohio Railway had come up Knapps Creek, through Huntersville and Frost. I have heard many times that the Chesapeake and Ohio people tried their very best to buy right of way down to Marlinton, because it would be so much easier to build a railroad from Marlinton to Durbin up this way. But all the farmers were against it. They said it would cut their farms to pieces, the trains would kill their cows and sheep, and the trains would scare their horses. They argued passionately against the trains. I heard that same argument in the 1920s when they took the highway through here. Farmers were still resistant, arguing that roads would cut their farms in two and scare their horses. The highway that's up here now [State Route 92]—they wanted it to stay right where it was, fording the creek,

Grandpa Jordan, circa 1905. Dr. Jordan supplemented his meager earnings as a county doctor by carrying the mail on horseback.

staying against the hills. [The railroad would eventually follow the Greenbrier River north from Marlinton to Durbin]
Shortly after we ate our lunch, we left Huntersville. There was nothing like mailboxes then. Every once in a while someone had a little wooden box that sat on a little post or something, but there were no enclosures. Most people who were expecting mail would just stand out to see if they had any or if the paper came along. We forded the creek where they were building a little concrete bridge. That was at a post office called Dilley's Mill, which is just below the scout camp. I remember my grandfather watering his horse and me watching the men working on the bridge while he went into the little post office. The bridge is still there. If you get out of your car and walk through the grass there, you can see it. They put a copper plate on the bridge with the year it was built, so you could find the year that I actually made that trip [1914].

I can remember my grandpa let the horse drink there and talked to the men who were building the bridge, and we drove into the creek to the post office. I waited in the buggy while he went in. He had a letter or two and I can remember he had a package when he came out. Then, in place of going back by the road, we went straight through the woods. There was a path up through the woods where you could ride or the buggy could go. And you came out right out where you enter Gordon and Mary Lou Dilley's farm. All through the hills I can't remember but one or two letters being picked up. The mail carrier would stop and talk. My grandpa would stop and visit with people for ten or fifteen minutes. We got back to Frost at about five o'clock in the evening.

A Movie and a Soda Pop

My grandfather—now, he was an unusual man for his time. My father took us to town often, but he was a farmer and a schoolteacher for ten years, and he wasn't interested in movies. My grandfather was the one who was the doctor. Dr. Jim Price said back then that if doctors went to school for two six-month terms, they were over-trained. That was the way with my Grandpa, who got his training in Washington and was used to going to events in the big city. So when we got down to Marlinton, the first thing he told my dad was that he was going to take me to the movies that night. He took me down to the movies, and it cost a nickel. I remember that it cost a nickel.

The movie house was the old Opera House in Marlinton. I was scared. He had to kind of console me because when all those things came at me on the screen, I wanted to get down behind my seat! However, he assured me that nothing would happen and that the action was just on the screen. When they changed the reels, I didn't know what they were doing. They just had one machine to run the film. That's why the reel had to be changed and also why the man was playing the piano. I have no idea what movie it was, nor who was playing the piano. I guess you could go back to history and find out. But it was a pretty place, the nicest place I had ever been in at the time. That was when it was new.

That was 1914. The next day, my dad went down on the street to the first bottling plant in Marlinton, which was Mason's Bottling Works. My dad knew Mr. Mason well. They were always talking about beagle hounds. He raised beagle hounds and my dad liked them. I well remember Mr. Mason was sitting on one of those straight chairs that you can rock back in and he was leaning back against the building with the front rungs up about six inches.

He looked at me and said, "I'm going to get the boy a bottle of pop." He talked really slowly. And he went in the building and got me a bottle of pop, and it was strawberry. There was no coke then. There was strawberry, lemon, orange, and cream soda. That was the first bottle of pop I ever had and it is actually the first bottle of pop I ever saw, I think. Well, it burned my tongue, and, if I wasn't careful when I was drinking it, my tongue would go into the bottle. I was between six and seven years old at the time, I'd say.

The One-Room School

You might like to know what the one-room schools were like in 1920. I went to a one-room school for seven years, from 1914 to 1921. There were no two-room schools in the area until after World War I. I went to school at Cove Hill because I lived on that farm across the hill from Frost and the nearest school was the little Cove Hill schoolhouse, which adjoined our farm. I started school when I was about seven years old and stayed there at Cove Hill until I finished the seventh grade.

My first teacher at Cove Hill was my aunt, Clara Jordan, and I considered her to be a very modern teacher. She had gone to Harrisonburg Normal School [today's James Madison University] because she had relatives all through there—Harrisonburg, Waynesboro, Luray. She got all of the samples she could get out of teacher magazines, like toothbrushes, toothpaste, and crayons. I saw my first toothpaste, Colgate's Ribbon Dental, and my first toothbrush there. She gave all the kids a toothbrush and a tube of Colgate's paste and showed us how to clean our teeth. Before that we had toothbrushes, but we always had to use salt or soda instead of the toothpaste.

There were about fifteen or twenty children who went to that school and the seats were double. Two children sat in a seat. There was an inkwell in the center because you didn't have ballpoint pens or anything. All you had was lead pencils or slate. Nobody was allowed to have ink in their inkwell until they got up to the fifth or sixth grade, because little kids would be spilling it all over everything. When you got older, the teacher would let you put ink in the inkwell. There was a little round hole in the top of the desk. There was a little glass bottle that fit down in that hole. The teacher would pour the ink in there and you could dip your pen down into the small neck of that. We used pencils that were called penny pencils. They were like pencils that we have now; only the rubber on the end of them wasn't enclosed in a metal casing. It was built right in the wood. Not very many people could afford anything but a penny pencil.

Kids were delighted when they had a tablet. We had tablets with real coarse paper where we wrote and did our arithmetic. It was fuzzy paper. It was coarser and wasn't slick like paper is now. If you had to write a story for class or something like that, some of the students would have a tablet and we guarded those tablets just like we were looking over gold. We kept those in a special place. There was a drawer, just a sliding place, to keep your books under the top of the desk. We kept the paper in that special place and those kids who couldn't afford paper had a slate.

They had a slate pencil as well. I really think they called it slate because it looked just like the slate that we'd see outside; only the slates were about twelve by twelve inches. Older slates were about six by eight—little ones. Those students did their arithmetic with a slate pencil. Then they would wipe off the writing with a rag. It wiped off better with a damp rag and. as you might imagine, most of the kids wrote on theirs and spit on it and wiped it off, which the teacher frowned upon very much. We didn't write anything with pen until we got into about sixth grade. Then the teacher, if you didn't have white paper, gave you white paper and you learned to write neatly with ink. That pen was just a straight instrument with a pen point that you pushed on. You learned how to use those and how not to smear your ink. That privilege was reserved for the upper grades.

The subjects we had were reading, writing, and math. Above the blackboard was always the ABCs written there beautifully. Most teachers wrote very, very well. Penmanship was prized back then. Sometimes there would be something like, "Do unto others as you would have them do unto you" written across there and you were to copy that. That was your penmanship training. First, you would learn to do the ABCs. There were two rows of them. One was the little ones, and the others were capitals.

Reading, writing, arithmetic, and English were what you started out with. And when I say English is what you started with, I mean you started with pronunciation. They taught you how to say words. So many children came to school who mispronounced words. Then they taught you how to spell the words. Then they taught you what the words meant. That's sort of the way you went up through your English.

When you got up to sixth grade, you started on hygiene and had some physiology and anatomy. In that way, you learned vocabulary that showed your hands, your shoulder, your feet, your hip, your eye, and your nose. Then they also had a book about agriculture when you got to the seventh or eighth grade. Really, to me that was one of the best subjects we had. That taught you all the animals on the farm from mice all the way to horses. You learned the names, the breeds of sheep, the breeds of cattle, and the breeds of horses. You looked at many pictures of them as well. Agriculture showed you something about growing wheat, oats, buckwheat, corn, and hay. There weren't any varieties of hay like we have now. There were really just native grasses, but it did show you those things. There were some weeds that it pictured in there also. To me it was altogether a little bit of zoology, a little bit of botany, and a little bit of biology. It just gave you a little taste of those things. I'm sorry that that doesn't exist now. I've seen kids who didn't know one cow from another or one horse from another. Most all of the kids then could tell you a Clydesdale from a Percheron. They could tell you a Dorset sheep from a Southdown. In pigs, they could tell you a Berkshire from a Poland China. If I say that to high school kids now, they don't even know that I'm talking about a pig.

I think elementary or one-room schools give you much more diversified education than the average kid gets up to the eighth grade today. When you got to the seventh or eighth grade, you knew all the verbs and adverbs. You could pick all those words out and name them as verbs, adverbs, adjectives, and pronouns. You learned a lot of conjugation and you learned tense. The big reason I think you learned that so well was because younger children who listened carefully started hearing the seventh and eighth grade children go over their work, and by the time a reasonably bright sixth grader was in the eighth grade, he or she knew all that. It was just repetition. So when they got out they were pretty well versed in their English. I got all the way through high school and college on just about what I learned in elementary school, because they didn't teach any more grammar than that.

The only extra thing I learned in high school was that Mrs. Fannie Overholt, my senior English teacher, made you learn a poem. And that poem had to be by a famous poet like Tennyson or Byron. I mean it was a real poem. Every Monday morning when you were a senior, you had to know the poem she assigned to you. And you really had to learn it. If you didn't know it when she called on you on Monday in your English class, you sat right there until dark and wrote it on the blackboard until you could say it from memory. I only had to write it one time because I knew she meant business. I learned a lot from that activity. When I got to college, the basic part of what I had to do in college English was composition and rhetoric, the writing part. I could parse, conjugate, and diagram a sentence. That was just old stuff. You just sat and slept through the class.

Everybody walked to school. I walked to Cove Hill School. I walked to Frost. I went to Frost the last two months because Cove Hill that year [1914–15] did not have enough students to run a full year. If they didn't have ten students, they had to end the term. The full year was six months and we only had enough students to run three months. That's the year Margie Herold was my teacher. There were so many kids at the Frost school that there was no seat for me, so my dad took a seat from the Cove Hill School and brought it over to Frost for me. He returned it at the end of the year. He was that interested in my going to school! My father always told us kids when we were small, "You are all going to school. You are all going to graduate from high school if I live." And I guess we all did. It was part of his dedication to the idea that you educate yourself out of poverty. I truly believe the kids learned more in the one-room schools [than in the consolidated schools of today]. My dad was the only one in this district who wanted a longer school year. Some parents said, "If you change to seven months, I won't send my kids." But when they read that you could be fined or jailed if your children were truant, they sent their kids!

When I was a child in school you had to read to the class. Then maybe the next time you had to read a story and tell it to the class. They went around and around that way and it gave you practice in reading and comprehension. Then, when you read and told a story, it improved your memory. It improved your delivery. Actually it was teaching you public speaking and also how to retain story details. That's why I like *McGuffey's Readers.* I'm too young to have studied *McGuffey's Readers.* They were already laid aside when I started, but I loved to read the things and that's where most of the stories that we read as children came from. Those were the stories we told to the classes.

Most of us kids who liked to read or tell stories got a big kick out of reading *The Knights of the Round Table,* the King Arthur stories, and *Sinbad the Sailor.* Most of the stories in those readers usually had a moral or they ended up with something good. The stories weren't scary or anything. They were just adventure stories that kids liked to hear. If you were a good listener, you could guess what was going to happen by the end. You didn't leave kids uptight or anything. They knew all the answers by the time you finished a story.

War Strikes

During the last century, during my lifetime, we have made slow progress from an agricultural society to an industrial society. When I was small, before World War I, you traveled by horse and buggy or by walking and you cultivated your fields by horse or by hand. World War I changed us. We learned about Europe, that's the first thing. Before the war, in school, the Western hemisphere was so isolated that only the intellectuals or the very rich knew anything about Europe. After that, we studied a lot more geography and history of Europe.

To promote the war, we had a burst of industrialism. Factories and plants were built quickly to prepare equipment, vehicles, ammunition, and everything like that. The war was a stimulus to people to invent. Research got a real boost. Although research grew in industry, it also did in medicine, education, and government. Newspapers became common. There were few publications that people had, especially in rural areas. But I was fortunate, I guess. I grew up in a home where there was a daily paper. The paper we read was T*he Cincinnati Post*. It came the next day and I can remember having the funnies read to me long before I went to school. But nobody else I can remember in the community had a daily paper.

I was born December 30, 1907. I was nine when the United States entered World War I in 1917. World War I really started in 1914 in Europe. We'd read about it a little in history and my dad or grandfather would read about it in the paper and tell us kids some of it. I don't remember a whole lot of what they said. I can remember when they told me that Germans were overrunning Belgium and I remember talking about trench warfare, which was totally new to us.

We learned the name of generals and we heard a lot about President Woodrow Wilson. I probably knew as much about Wilson when I was in the eighth grade as I did about any other president. As a matter of fact, he's probably the only one I could tell you anything much about. Even though my parents were Republicans, they had high respect for Woodrow Wilson. I think Wilson was fifty years ahead of his time. Wilson thought that maybe one day the world would be so close together that maybe one government would be sufficient for the entire world. I don't think that can happen. The reason why the United States and Great Britain get along so well together is that they speak the same language. The reason that Yugoslavia is so fragmented is that they speak all different languages and two or three of their languages have completely different alphabets.

I don't remember being scared a bit of the war. Some of my neighbors were there and at my age it just seemed like really a big deal to get in the service and to go to Europe. Most thought it was a big honor to go, wanted to go, and enjoyed it. All the soldiers I knew from this area returned safely and they had great stories to tell us kids. All I remember about the war ending was the headline from *The Cincinnati Post* in 1918, "Armistice Signed," and that's about all there was to it. It was very quiet here. It would be mentioned at meetings and about the only meeting that you went to was something at school or church. Those were the only places you would hear about such things. In rural communities like this, nobody went to Marlinton because we were too far away. The roads weren't good enough unless you could spend a day going down and a day coming back. That only happened once or twice a year when you needed clothes or something like that.

During the war industry picked up. For the first time lots of common people traveled to Europe and became familiar with a larger world. Everybody in the community realized that there was somewhere else other than West Virginia and the United States. We began to talk about France, Germany, Belgium, Italy - Italy is about the only one that you ever heard about here because the county had a lot of Italian immigrants. The railroads in this county were practically built by Italians. They evidently knew more about building railroads than the native people. I was always in school with some Italian kids. But other than Italy, we didn't know anything about Europe until the war.

Political Changes and the Family

My dad was a non-drinker and a non-tolerator of drink. Therefore Prohibition wasn't discussed. He was just glad to see it, but before it was over, he was convinced that it wasn't doing what it should because lots of the families down through the community were making their own liquor. Prohibition came in 1920 and was done by 1933.

I can remember when women got the vote in 1920. Women did not vote when I was a child and I can remember when my dad took my mother down to vote. My mother voted the first time women were able to vote. My dad took her to vote and I don't think they voted the same ticket. Whenever she asked him how she should vote, he just said, "Suit yourself." That was his only answer. I don't think more than half of the women here started voting then. There are plenty of women who don't vote now. They just don't want to go to the polls and a few of the religious groups think that men should do all the governing. But all of my family has voted.

The End of the Farm

Years later, in 1962, I moved back to Frost, to this farm where I live now, but I was born and raised on the one up the road. That is the farm that four generations of Sharps were raised on and it's still owned by a relative. My dad sold it to my mother's sister's daughter and her husband, Clarence and Ena Buzzard. They were trying to keep it in the family. He sold the farm because the taxes and cost of running it had grown to be as great as his gross income. In 1932 the state passed the Tax Limitation Amendment. If that had been in effect, my dad never would have sold the farm.

But he wanted to educate his kids. There were three boys and we have five degrees among us, I guess. All of us went to college. My dad believed in college. He graduated from the Edray Normal School in 1898. [As I said,] his statement to us kids was "You don't dig your way out of poverty. You educate your way up."

A Boy Goes to Town

1921–1926

"Until I read it in the paper, I never knew
I was an underprivileged child."
—Dr. Sharp, quoting Groucho Marx

I went to the school at Cove Hill until I finished seventh grade. Then I went to eighth grade in Raywood. I went to Raywood one year because my mother's sister [Clara Jordan] was a schoolteacher and she taught at Raywood. She married the business manager of the Warn Lumber Company. They persuaded my family to send me over with them for a year because my school year at Cove Hill was six months then, and in Raywood the school year was nine months. Schools like Cass[1] and Raywood were nine months because West Virginia Pulp and Paper and Warn Lumber companies paid the teachers the extra three months of salary.

Now, Raywood was four miles down from Cass. It was on the east side of the Greenbrier River, on the other side from Cass. It was owned by the Warn Lumber Company, which also had a band mill and an operation at Stamping Creek. They came from Stamping Creek to Raywood and put that town in. They had a double band sawmill and had two train engines at Raywood. Eventually they owned all of the land that is now the Monongahela National Forest, beginning at Sam Harper's property clear back to Virginia and all the way to Dunmore. They owned all of that forest. They bought the forest to get the

[1] Cass was the company town of the largest timbering and saw mill operation in Pocahontas County. Established in 1901 and in operation until 1960, today it is the Cass Scenic Railroad State Park, with 100 year old steam locomotives offering excursions to the top of Bald Knob and best preserved former logging town in West Virginia

Roland Sharp, age 13, at his at his Aunt Clara Jordan's house in Raywood.

lumber. When they closed, they sold most of it to the federal government.

Raywood probably had five hundred to one thousand people. They didn't have a doctor. The doctor came from Cass about three times a week. The doctor walked down the track. Raywood had a large company store. Their trains were gear-driven like the Cass trains with their Shay engines. They ran on the standard gauge rails. It wasn't a dinky-type railroad.

The millions of board feet of lumber that they shipped out of Raywood were loaded onto boxcars, and their engines pushed it across the Greenbrier River and over the bridge to the siding[2]. The C&O trains just picked it all up on the siding. That's the way Cass shipped all of their lumber, and Raywood shipped theirs too.

High School Begins in Cass

In the fall of 1922, my aunt found out that they were going to have ninth grade at Cass that very year. Cass had a ninth grade before there were school buses and before the roads were good enough to support that type of transportation. So my aunt persuaded my mother to send me back to live with her for another year and let me go to school at Cass for the ninth grade. Cass was four miles up the railroad track from Raywood, and I walked with three other boys. I don't think we missed a day that winter. The road from Cass to Green Bank, where the high school was located, was not graveled completely and they couldn't run a bus, but they had enough kids at Cass to justify having a ninth grade class there.

Aside from the three boys I walked to school with from Raywood, along the way at Deer Creek we picked up another boy who walked with us into Cass. His father was the superintendent of the extract plant that was at Deer Creek,

[2] Siding is a separate section of track, alongside the generally travelled track, sometimes used during loading and unloading, or connecting additional cars.

halfway between Raywood and Cass. That plant processed a dye from red oak bark and hemlock bark. It was a huge plant and it produced a huge quantity of that dye. Maybe a dozen tank cars stood along the track every day.

The dye was khaki-colored only. It was said back at that time that that plant produced all the khaki coloring for the uniforms in World War I—the American uniforms, that is. Of course, that plant went out of business as soon as chemical dyes were manufactured. Chemical dyes were made from aniline or other chemical substances that proved more effective and efficient to produce than the old extract dye. The extract dyes were a very fine industry for this area because farmers could take a load of bark in any time, in the same way that people take truckloads of pulpwood to the paper mill in Covington today. If a family needed a little extra money, they could bring a load of bark to the extract plant.

Well, I might mention this. The school at Cass must have been the biggest in the county. There must have been close to 400 students there, and students did not change rooms. There were so many students that it created too much chaos for all of them to move from room to room, so the teachers changed rooms instead. I think it would've torn the building down if we students had all changed classes at once! The Cass mill was running many trains onto Cheat Mountain daily, taking off trainloads of logs. And around three o'clock of an evening they would start coming in, and school would almost end then because the trains would be shifting the cars and the bells and whistles would be blowing constantly. You know how it is on sidings. One train would come in, and as soon as it came, another would follow, until you could hardly hear the teachers' voices after that.

As far as I remember we had a course in math, freshman English, and a class in ancient history. The other course was general science. We made a yearbook at Cass that we just handwrote and put Kodak pictures in, but mine was lost years ago.

It's hard to believe, but the students who reached the top of the class were those you never would have guessed would succeed. You just thought that the lawyers' and doctors' and superintendents' children were going to automatically become great, but it didn't turn out that way!

As far as the town of Cass is concerned, it was really an active place. The company store had everything. You could buy anything, from a box of tacks to a Cadillac. You just had to go in and tell them what you wanted and they would get it for you. There were other stores like department stores. There were several, but the most important ones were Brill's Store and Cooper's Store. Other than those extra stores, the company store had a department store, a drug store, and a snack bar where you could get sodas and ice creams. They also had a pharmacist.

Believe it or not, there were two tailor shops at Cass that would make you a full suit of clothes. All you did was go into the tailor shop and get measured. They would take the cloth down, just the way you would go into the store and get broadcloth. You'd pick the bolt of cloth you liked, they would measure you for the suit, the next week he had it cut out and pinned together and adjusted the fit, and the following week you got your suit. One of the tailor shops was where I got my first pair of long pants. I was a small kid and so were two or three other of the boys in that ninth grade. Well, the problem for me was that you didn't get to wear long pants until you were five feet tall or more. It was thought totally abominable for youngsters to wear long pants. It didn't matter how old you were, just how tall! There were at least three in that class who wore short pants. Thankfully, I was graduated to long pants. My suit was ordered from Sears, Montgomery Ward, or somewhere like that, but we had to take it to Andy Sisco's tailor shop on the east side of the river to be properly fitted.

There were people on the streets of Cass all day long and the stores and the trains were constantly busy. The one thing Cass didn't have was a bank. Durbin had a bank, Hillsboro had a bank, and Marlinton had two and later three banks. Farmers and Merchants was the third bank in Marlinton. The banks were closed in 1933 when Franklin Roosevelt became president.

Roosevelt closed all of the banks for a week or so to take an audit or to check the condition of the bank. All of the banks in this county were okay. The only one that stayed closed for three or four weeks was the First National Bank. The Bank of Pendleton [County] in Franklin failed. It did not have enough funds to continue, so the Farmers and Merchants in Marlinton, which was in the old Alpine Hotel building, moved to Franklin. The old Farmers and Merchants Bank is now the Pendleton County Bank, with the home office in Franklin.

I should also mention that I think the ninth grade was only there for one year. They had finished graveling the road from Cass to Green Bank and a bus was put on it the next year. It carried those kids to Green Bank, where they graduated. West Virginia Pulp and Paper [which owned the Cass operation] paid for the buses. They weren't really buses, though. They were trucks with seats on the sides. The state didn't approve buses until 1932.

My classmates all went to Green Bank High School, except one other boy and me. We went to Edray District High School in Marlinton. We both graduated from there in 1926.

To School, by Train or through Mud

I went to ninth grade in Cass. Then I went to Marlinton. Almost every district had a high school after World War I, but Huntersville District didn't have enough money or enough kids to build one. So the Huntersville District Board of Education donated five or ten dollars, something like that, to the Edray or Green Bank District High School for each Huntersville student who went there. Back at that time I was not familiar with the financial set up of the school.

There were about 250 kids when I went to Edray District High School. That's what Marlinton High School was called before the present county school system came into being in 1933.

Edray District High School, Marlinton, WV, in 1926.
Roland Sharp graduated from here that year.

Before that, when I went to school, it was by district and each district had its own board of education. Hillsboro had the first high school, Little Levels District High School. Marlinton was the second to have a high school and it was called Edray District High School. Green Bank District got a high school in 1917.

Well, at that time my home was in Frost, and it was easier for me to go to Marlinton than to attempt to go to Green Bank, because you could get boarding in Marlinton. They didn't have any boarding houses or anything in the Green Bank area. I went to Marlinton because of places that my family could get for me to board down there. You had to board in town or stay with relatives because there were no buses. The roads were so muddy that if you went to Marlinton after October you had to ride a horse or walk.

I boarded with S.L. Brown, the county clerk. He was the county clerk from the time the courthouse opened in Marlinton until he died, except for one term—for almost thirty years. He lived alone, but he had a housekeeper. He allowed the housekeeper to keep boarders for her pay. She fed him and kept his house, and in turn she kept four boys as boarders and collected the rent for her salary. Boarding was really cheap, maybe ten or fifteen dollars a month. Since I was a kid, I didn't have any idea what it was. Kids didn't ask their parents what they were paying for them. Did you?

Stanley McLaughlin from Stony Bottom went to Marlinton, too, because you could go from Stony Bottom to Marlinton on the train every day. Marlinton had four trains. The first train in the morning came down from Durbin and arrived around eight o'clock. Then at seven o'clock in the evening that train came back from Ronceverte, went to Winterburn, and stayed all night. So students from Raywood and Stony Bottom who went to high school [before there was a ninth grade at Cass] could ride the train down in the morning. They would be there real early and then go home at seven in the evening. That's how Stanley

McLaughlin came from Stony Bottom. He'd ride down at eight in the morning and come back at seven in the evening.

It was a long, long day, but when you lived up here in Frost, the road was not graded. It was graded up to Huntersville. They were working on Knapps Creek grading the road. It was so muddy and bad that it was difficult in a buggy or wagon to go over the road. So I had to walk to Marlinton or walk home when we wanted to come home on the weekend, or we could ride to Harter on the train and walk across Thorny Creek Mountain. That was a little easier and shorter. When I graduated, this road was not even graveled. They had finished the grading of the road, but there was no improvement of the road.

Metropolitan Marlinton

Marlinton seemed like a big town when I went to high school there. The Alpine Hotel was on the corner where the First Citizens bank is now. The hotel later burned down. The theater, the Farmers & Merchants bank, and the hotel were all on that big corner, and there was a restaurant in the back. You went around the corner on Second Avenue and went in the restaurant on the side at the back part of the hotel. On Main Street in Marlinton, there was no diner. The first building there was Key and McNeil's Drug Store. There is sort of a humorous side to the drugstores. Key and McNeil's drugstore was always considered the one where the Republican students hung out, and Doc Allen's Royal Drug Store was where the Democrat students hung out. They both had soda fountains and everything. So the Republicans stayed over at Key and McNeil's, and the Democrats stayed over at the Royal.

The second building was Johnson's Restaurant. The third building was Thomas's Grocery and the next one on the corner was Wilber Sharp's poolroom. Then across the street was the Bank of Marlinton, the Royal Drug Store, and Schuchat's Department Store, and the next one on the corner was

Kelmenson's Department Store. They both closed early in the Depression. S. B. Wallace's wholesale drug place was just around the corner. At one time S. B. Wallace was one of the biggest wholesale druggists in West Virginia. They shipped to nearly every county in West Virginia and adjoining states. Had it not been a family business, it could have been a great thing even today in Marlinton.

T. J. Mason had the pop plant on Third Avenue. It would be right about where the back of the First National Bank is now. That was T. J. Mason's Bottling Works.

Also right below where the diner now stands, on Third Avenue, was a barbershop. It was also a bath house where people who came from the timbering camps could get their hair cut, then pay a quarter and go back in the back rooms, where they could shower or get in the tub and soak and clean up. I remember going in there for a haircut and seeing people come in and give the barber a quarter, then go through that back door. I was too young to really know what the place was, but later when I grew up I found out that that's where you came in to get a haircut, shave, and take a bath.

The first hard road or macadam was from Marlinton to Campbelltown. Everybody who went to Marlinton went across the bridge to Brill's Store to see the hard-surfaced road. I know the first time I went to town after the road was surfaced to Campbelltown. We went across the bridge to Brill's to look at the road. Anybody who owned an automobile in the county always rode up to Campbelltown to try out that hard-surfaced road. I believe the reason for the hard surface was that the road led to the fairgrounds, and our fair was the state's biggest for many years.

The road from Frost to Marlinton was not graveled so that you could run a bus over it, probably until 1928 or 1929. That's when they started running buses from Frost to Marlinton. Mr. Ward Harper, he owned the bus system. We weren't under the county system, so there were no county-owned buses. Private people owned the buses. It was really a truck that ran from Cass

SENECA

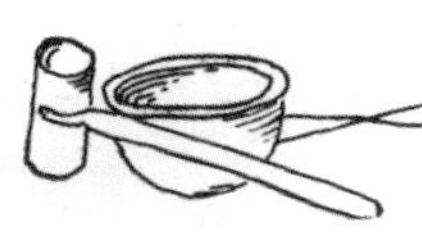

MIRIAM B. DUVALL
Latin Club, '23, W. H. S.; French Club, '23, W. H. S.; Astronomy Club, '23, W. H. S.; Le Cercle Francais, '26; Seneca Staff, '26.

→ROLAND P. SHARP
Basketball, '23; Track, '25; Football, '25; M-Club, '25; Glee Club, '26; Seneca Staff, '26.

ETHEL M. LIVESAY
Katchy-Koo, '23; Glee Club, '23, '24; Basketball, '25; President Le Cercle Francais, '26; Assistant Editor Seneca Staff, '26.

OKIE WALTON
Le Cercle Francais, '26.

MARY RUTH GWIN
Le Cercle Francais, '26.

ROBERT M. BARLOW
Vice-President, '22, '23.

FLORENCE RANDOLPH PRICE
Katchy-Koo, '23; President 4-H Club, '23; Glee Club, '23, '24, '25, '26; Basketball, '25; Seneca Staff, '26; Assistant Editor "Pocahontas History of School Staff," '25; Best All-round Girl, '26; May Parcher, "Seventeen," '26.

Roland Sharp second from the top, in the 1926 "Seneca," the yearbook of Edray District High School. Yearbook comments, "...has the most attractive drawl and is a wit, too..." "Probably will be a surgeon."

to Green Bank. Ward Harper had an old truck that he had converted, putting a roof on it. He picked students up along Knapps Creek and took them to Marlinton. That was 1928 or 1929, two years after I graduated.

High School Classes

I wasn't scared when I went to Marlinton. My dad had been a schoolteacher and my grandfather had been a doctor. He had lived in a log house that was built way before the Civil War. It's still standing and it's one of the two oldest houses in Frost. My grandfather migrated from Pendleton County over here and bought that house in 1900. My dad graduated from the Edray Normal School in 1898. Did you know that long before there were high schools there were normal schools? They were private higher education schools that qualified people to become teachers.

Every Wednesday we had an assembly. We, as students, hoped and prayed that our principal, Mr. G.D. McNeill, wouldn't be able to get anyone to speak at our assemblies. If no one spoke, if he couldn't get a speaker, he told a story from his years in the Navy when he traveled around the world with Theodore Roosevelt's Great White Fleet. He said it was to open up the world, but it was really to show the might of the United States. He probably had ten years' worth of stories. We would hope that scheduled assembly speakers wouldn't show up, so that Mr. McNeill would talk instead. We just sat there with our mouths open![3]

When I went to high school we had three lyceum courses in the winter. It was either music, dancing, or philosophical something. In college, at Concord, we had two or three lyceum courses that were part of your tuition. In the summer, we had two Chautauqua programs; mostly they were music. The

---

[3] For G.D. McNeill's accounts of Pocahontas County history, see *The Last Forest: Tales of the Allegheny Woods* [1999] and *Tales of Pocahontas County* [1994], both published by Pocahontas Communications Cooperative Corporation.

programs were designed in Chautauqua, New York. That was the excitement that we had as kids, lyceum and Chautauqua.

The Army's Influence

After World War I, all you heard was that it was the war to end all wars, and the world was going to be living at peace from then on. Our military totally changed. We had a very small army after the war. They had an ROTC [Reserve Officers' Training Corps] and a CMTC [Citizens' Military Training Camps] and an ORC [Officers' Reserve Corps]. After World War I, if you wanted a career in the Army, when you were in high school you could sign up with the CMTC. You went to high school in the winter, and in the summer term you went to a military training camp for basic training. If you got four summers of training and graduated from high school, you could take an examination for a second lieutenant's commission. That ran up to President Roosevelt's administration. The Officers' Reserve Corps was something like that, but you had to be a high school graduate to do that, and you followed that through until either you failed or you became a second lieutenant. And the ROTC was in the colleges and in army camps during the summers. About a third of the boys in my high school class went to CMTC in the summer. Only one stayed after high school and made the military a career. I had two summers and my dad insisted that I go to college, so I didn't complete the four years.

When you were in CMTC military training after World War I, you could go to Camp Knox, Kentucky for the summer and go to school for the winter. Then they would put you through military training. They put us boys in with the regular troops of the Tenth Infantry, three soldiers for each boy in an outfit. Back then you could join the Army or Navy for a year at a time. That's how little they were concerned about war in the future. Today, the commitment is three years or more. Back then, four summers counted for one year of official military training.

I went the summers of 1924 and 1925 to Camp Knox, Kentucky but I went to summer school in college in 1926, so I did not complete my year of military training. I think that was good plan and should be reinstated because it created discipline. Military training creates discipline in both men and women, but of course it was only men then. When you came back from one summer at Camp Knox, your whole demeanor had changed. When you took your socks off, you put them up. When you took your shoes off, you set them somewhere. You didn't leave your dirty underwear or towels lying around somewhere. You saw that they were washed, folded, and put in your locker. Those habits carry over into the rest of your life in a positive way.

When my grandchildren come in my house and spend the night, they leave the bathroom or the bedroom a wreck. I guess I was the same way, but when I got back from the first summer of military training, I knew my parents could tell a big difference in the way I acted around the house. By the second summer, I was pretty well disciplined and that had a carryover when I went to summer school in college and when I went to the dormitory. My room looked different from the others—not that I was smarter or anything, but I had been taught that when you use the towel, you put the towel back on the rack. When you use the washcloth, you wash a washcloth and spread it out. When you take your dirty clothes off, you put them in a laundry bag. They were supposed to be washed every two or three days. You didn't leave them in there until they mold.

At Camp Knox we drilled in the morning and had a lot of exercise. That was good for your health, but in the afternoon all you did was sit and listen to civics lectures where they talked about peace and how the world would be at peace. They gave you some history, but there was nothing ever mentioned except Germany, France, Great Britain, Belgium, Holland, and the Norwegian area. There was no mention of India, the Middle East, Africa—none of that—because all of those were under France, Belgium, and Great Britain at the time. The British owned everything practically in the Middle East. That's why those people speak English now. The only other things I heard about were South Africa, Rhodesia, and maybe a little bit about Ethiopia.

I don't believe that they thought that there were any significant countries in the world other than the United States, France, Great Britain, and Germany. That was about the world. That's where medicine and industry were being developed. Maybe part of that was lack of communication. They probably didn't know anything about the rest of the world. You never read much about foreign countries in a newspaper back then.

We always had a daily paper in our house, *The Cincinnati Post.* Before I could read, my grandpa or dad would read me the funny papers.

Opportunity in the Twenties

In the early 1900s, when kids had an opportunity to leave this county, they did. This was before I can remember, but Frank and Hanson Sharp from this area went to Panama to work on the Panama Canal. A whole group of people from Pocahontas County went to Ohio, Indiana, and other states, even as far as Idaho. You will find Buzzards in Iowa and even in the Dakotas who originally came from this county. In the last twenty five years I have seen some of their offspring who have come back here to look around for relatives. I can't give you any good reason why they left. There was just nothing around here for them to do except farm, I guess. They probably wanted to get away from home. After the Civil War there was just a constant movement from the east to the west. A lot of my relatives on my mother's side moved to Indiana. Most of them went for land grants out west.

Louis Carpenter was the only one who came back and he walked all the way back from Iowa, the story goes, because he missed the sound of Buster Bowers' hounds chasing foxes on Michael Mountain.

There wasn't any opportunity for people here in the twenties other than for men in the lumbering business. We had two tanneries, three or four big sawmills, and finishing-type mills. Those at Cass, Nottingham, Raywood, and Clover Lick were the major ones. Mountain Grove and Raywood are nothing but farms now. There was also an extract plant that prepared die from bark for khaki uniforms worn by American soldiers in World War I. Just as soon as chemical dyes came into existence, that just died overnight. That was when I was in high school or college. They had two to four hundred employees.

Hoover and the Depression

This country has had one engineer as president, and he is the one who standardized everything from nuts to bolts. Before that, if you bought a bicycle that had a bolt on it, you might have to go to ten stores before you could find a bolt that was the right size. If you did, you might not find a nut that fit the threads of the bolt. That came about in the twenties. That president was Herbert Hoover, the most maligned one. The people in this country probably owe Herbert Hoover more than they realize. He standardized everything; nails, nuts, bolts, screws, doors, windows, and beds. Every factory that made mattresses had its own sizes. They made doors different sizes. It was difficult to replace everyday objects due to the lack of standardization of sizes and specifications. Hoover's role in implementing that standardization should be publicized more, because it has improved our quality of life considerably.

That was publicized some back in the thirties and forties when he got such a bad name for the Depression. It was no more his idea to have the Depression than it would be Franklin Roosevelt's. Hoover just happened to be in office when everything came crashing down. Of course, he got the blame for it. Those who were trying to help him later published articles about his positive contributions or I never would have known about them. Magazines wrote the pros and the cons in their columns. All the bad things that were attributed to him and then all the good things that were attributed to him were catalogued there. Another important contribution was his being the person who furnished the food and fed Europe after World War I. They were in poverty and totally in starvation. Hoover helped formulate a plan to restore Europe after World War I in the same way the Marshall Plan did that after World War II. Hoover went to Belgium to do that because Belgium was totally destroyed after that war. He gained a worldwide reputation for that. Then later he got a worldwide reputation for being responsible for the Depression. Then later he got the reputation for being the guy that standardized everything that was manufactured in this country.

The big timber companies here had cut back by the Depression. You couldn't sell lumber then anywhere. You could buy the finest flooring for fifty dollars a thousand board feet; birch, red oak, or maple hardwood. It came in bundles that you could piece together until you couldn't even see the cracks, and they couldn't sell it for fifty dollars a thousand.

In '26 or '27 fewer jobs were available. After 1930 or '31 none of those plants, including the tanneries and the mills, were selling anything. They just laid the workers off. The county was full of those unemployed people. No new industries came in. It seems to me that this county had quite a few more people in 1920 than it does now.

People are far less caring now than they were then. During the Depression people were interested in seeing that their neighbors had food, medical care, and clothing. However, after we become prosperous, after the Second World War, it seemed like the war changed the attitude of people. The attitude became, "Your business is your business. My business is mine. Stay out of it." We became more mobile and families split up. Then the roads reached the place where you could travel by automobile. The younger ones went various places to work. They married someone there, and then settled in different areas.

In this area, you didn't really know there was a Depression. I'm sort of like Groucho Marx, who made the statement, "Until I read it in the paper, I never knew I was an underprivileged child." I grew up, graduated from high school, started to college, and I didn't know that there was a Depression. We didn't start talking about the Depression until the middle of the thirties. We just thought, "Times are hard. Money is scarce." But this is a rural county. Everybody had food and the majority of people had clothes. We weren't used to having money. Until after we became industrialized, people didn't look at money as something that you were striving for. What you were striving for was your food, your clothing, and your shelter, and some for improving education in their family. As well as I remember, in the teens and the twenties people here got what they needed by raising cattle and sheep. Their wool, their chickens, and their eggs bought their necessities.

Music and the Radio

One of my sisters, Clarabelle, the youngest one, was very musical. The family had a pump-type organ. She learned to play that and she was the organist at the church from the time she was about ten years old. We bought a piano and she learned to play swing on it. We bought that piano in the late twenties, a Baldwin studio-type. It only cost two hundred dollars, and you paid only two dollars a month toward it. I don't know where it came from. I just answered an ad in the newspaper.

You still see the same ads, "Piano for sale." And it will say that a piano in your community has to be picked up, or it's being turned back in for nonpayment.

Back then, you didn't call on the telephone. You wrote. So, I wrote and asked them where the piano was and one day somebody appeared at the house with the piano on a little old truck. They said, "This is the piano that's for sale." It was a brand-new Baldwin. Baldwin made excellent pianos. So we paid two dollars a month, which was difficult to get.

When I was about a sophomore in high school, I got a guitar for Christmas and we played together. Clarabelle was very talented. She could play the piano, and later she could play the accordion and learned the violin by the time she was through high school. She spent a winter or two with one of my mother's sisters in Pennsylvania, close to Chautauqua, New York, and that was one of the music capitals of the country at that time. That's where all of your lyceums or Chautauqua numbers for school came from. Clarabelle died with a strep infection in 1937—that was common in those days.

I always liked music and as soon as I could afford it, I got a little portable Victrola that you cranked. You know they made those don't you? Victor made one with a dog on it. That was the best, but very few could afford that. They were tall. I bought one of those at a sale and gave it to one of my grandchildren recently. But I bought one of the little ones that you crank up and I bought every record of popular music I could afford and played them constantly. You could order records from Sears, Roebuck or Montgomery Ward, or the jewelry store sometimes would sell them to you. But most of the time you ordered them from those mail-order houses. They were Victor and Edison records. And there were country singers like Vernon Dalhart. He was a real popular one back then. I think that the first record I got for the little crank Victrola was "Charlie My Boy" and another one, "Yes, We Have No Bananas." Have you heard of those? On records they had "The Wreck of the Shenandoah," about the huge dirigible that crashed in Cambridge, Ohio. Every time there was a calamity in this country there were songs written, and those were popular songs at that time. I remember that music well.

I remember the first radio that I ever heard was at Frost at the old store. It was an Atwater Kent. It had three dials on the front you had to work. You could hear a voice just about like you could on a good telephone. My telephone, which has no volume control, was just about as loud as that thing. There was so much static that you would just be hearing something like the best part of the news and then you'd just hear sounds like popcorn popping. You couldn't hear any of it or it would squall real loud, a great old big long whistle. I think the first big group of people that gathered at the Frost store's radio was [in 1926 or 1927] to listen to the Gene Tunney–Jack Dempsey prizefight. That was maybe the first prizefight that was broadcast and the store was full. Individuals didn't have radios. I can remember that night. Every time the fight got interesting, the static would come on or one of those long whistles would pierce our ears. Then everybody would just wonder what happened!

People didn't have radios until the late twenties. Can you imagine what a radio in the twenties was like? You could only get three or four stations. KDKA [Pittsburgh], WLS Sears, Roebuck [Chicago], and WLW in Cincinnati were the big ones, and a lot of what they broadcast was music, not much discussion. Did you know that WLS stands for "world's largest store"? There was evening news and "Amos and Andy," and then from then on until one or two o'clock in the morning was time for the big bands. There were no good radios before the thirties. The music was late at night. You would start getting good reception about ten o'clock at night and from then on until four o'clock in the morning, reception would be excellent, but almost all the stations would sign off by two o'clock. Then when you turned it on in the morning, the reception was terrible.

The first radio I had I rented, for three dollars a month. After the third payment, Mr. Jennings said, "Just keep it—it sells for fifteen dollars!" I listened a lot. I was a fan of the big bands. As soon as we could afford it, around 1935, radios began to get good, with big boomers on them that you could really hear. We bought a really good one, from Montgomery Ward. We would have our supper listening to Lowell Thomas, the news—that was at six o'clock—and then "Amos and Andy," and then probably nothing else of any significance for an hour or two until the big bands would come on; Glenn Miller, Tommy Dorsey, Shep Fields, all of those. We'd turn that thing on and go to bed and fall asleep listening to it. You didn't have to worry about turning it off because they turned it off for you!

You've heard of the Edgewater Beach Hotel? The Sherman in Chicago? The Drake, the Morrison? They all had a big-time band and they just advertised the hotel with their band on the radio. I expect that at that time I could have written down the names of at least thirty big bands that were playing swing. I don't know exactly when I became a fan of Big Band music, but I sure grew to love it. In later years I stayed at the Drake and the Sherman, just to say I slept where those big bands were.

A Student and a Teacher

1926–1938

"Stand up bravely, speak out plainly, sit down quickly. Do not speak more than 15 minutes, or you may tell more than you know."

—Dr. Sharp's public speaking professor

I'll say this about my dad. He was education-conscious. He graduated from the Edray Normal School in 1898. He taught school from 1898 to 1907 and in 1908 the salary was so little that he just went back to farming full time. However, he told us when we were very small kids, "All of you are going to get a high school education. I'm going to see to that." All the boys graduated from high school. There were three boys and the three of us had five college-earned degrees. Two of the three girls graduated from high school, the other almost did, and then they were married.

College Makes a Teacher

My graduation from high school in 1926 ended my farming days because [then] I went to Concord College. My dad saw that I was motivated to go on further because as soon as I graduated, he started talking about going on to school. He told me at the time, "I can't afford to send you, but I'm going to borrow a hundred dollars against the farm. If you'll pay it back, I'm going to borrow it from the bank. I want you to go for the summer to Concord College, either Concord or Elkins, or one of the normal schools for the summer program." I chose Concord because Guy Bambrick, who was one of our neighbors, was going to Concord, and I knew Guy pretty well. My dad talked with him. I talked

Roland Sharp, student at Concord State Normal School in 1928. He could afford to attend Concord only two full school years. The rest of his work was done a term or summer session at a time.

to my dad and convinced him that it would be better for me to go to Concord because it was cheaper, even though it was farther. Tuition was only ten dollars and the health and activity fee was $2.50. That was per semester, summer term or semester, either one.

That's how I got started going to college. If you were the least bit interested in school, one summer session motivated you to go on. Once I had that first summer, I just couldn't miss another summer term. I went to college every time I had enough money to go a semester. I went to Concord [Concord State Normal School] the summer of 1926, which automatically gave me a one-year first-class teaching certificate. If you had taken that normal training in high school and then gone to one of the state normal schools [the term for teacher training schools back then] for the summer term and got nine hours of college credit, you automatically got a teacher's certificate for one year. Mr. Hevener Dilley was on the Board of Education for this district and he immediately hired me to teach at the Bethel School, which was located on the Hill Road, a hundred yards from the Bethel Church. That's where I taught the first six months term. I got seventy five dollars and I taught six months. I liked teaching. If the salary had been good enough to live on, I would have lived and died a schoolteacher.

During those [next] ten years, I taught at six one-room schools and kept going to college whenever I could. In the 1930 to '31 term I completed my junior year. I went summers in 1931 through 1936, and graduated in 1936. I had 146 semester hours when I graduated, but the reason I went so much longer is that it took so long from when I started that requirements would change over time and I would have to take those new courses. So even the last semester I was there I had three or four required courses that had been put in the curriculum between the time I started and then. I took my first summer term in 1926 and I graduated in 1936. I often tell people who don't know me that I started school in 1926 and I was so dumb that I didn't graduate until 1936, ten years later. However, in the meantime I had taught school for ten years in the one-room schools. And I met more people going summers, because teachers came to take classes, and we had visiting faculty teaching from all over.

I used to have panic attacks. I never knew what a panic attack was and I never had one when I got up in front of my students, but if I had to make a speech on the same thing out somewhere else, my tie would just flop up and down. I could feel my heart beat. No one else could see that or tell [that I had the problem].

The way I think I probably got over that is I somehow convinced myself that I knew as much as anybody about the topic and if they knew more, they'd be the ones up there talking. You have to sell yourself to you. That's how you get over it. The other thing I learned was never try to talk about things that you don't know thoroughly. That's what gives panic attacks—not knowing your subject well enough. I was forced to take public speaking and at first I had panic attacks three times a week. But the public speaking teacher used to say, "Stand up bravely, speak out plainly, sit down quickly. Do not speak more than fifteen minutes or you may tell more than you know."

Too many people try to make speeches on things that they don't know. I got that through my head when I was going to Concord State Normal School [the college changed its name to Concord State Teachers College in 1931 and to Concord College in 1943. Its current name is Concord University]. Why should they teach you how to teach reading when you can't read? They spent time teaching me how to teach math and I kept saying, "I can't teach math if I don't know math. Teach me more math and I can teach the kids." Most of the teachers who couldn't teach reading or math—it was because they didn't know how to read or do math well.

My dad was a good mathematician. He just went to normal school and never went to college, but he learned more math [than I did]. Whenever I told him that I didn't understand a problem, his answer to me was, "There's only one thing wrong with you, young man. You can't read. If you can read it, it tells you exactly what to do. Can't you read?"

When I started teaching histology at the college level, the panic attacks left. I knew that I knew more about histology than any of the students, and I was thoroughly grounded in microscopic anatomy.

Love Strikes

After my first teaching job, I went back to Concord for another term. I met my first wife, Opal, in college in 1927. Our meeting was sort of a strange thing. When I saw her, she was the most beautiful girl I had ever seen. I said "If I could meet that one. That is probably the one that I would marry." In 1927 I was twenty years old and it took me three years to convince her of that, because she didn't believe that story. Many times she stood me up. I would extend an invitation such as, "Meet me" or "Could I go home with you?" or "Could I meet you here to go to the Sweet Shop or something like that after class?" She might respond, "If you are standing down here where you go out of the building, or if you're by the sundial or the library, yes." But when she came out that door, I found very quickly that if I wasn't standing right there on time, she wouldn't wait one minute. She'd walk right on up the street just as fast as she could walk. She did that with every boy. She was too good a looking woman to wait around for anybody. She didn't believe that any woman should be beholden to any man.

The second time I saw her, she was driving her car, an Anderson. I waved, but she just gave me an ugly face. That was the way she was. You weren't flirting with her!

She was a girl that was getting attention from all the men at school. So, I made little difference. But, I pursued that. Every time I saw her, I spoke to her and I asked her for a date. And, finally, she did consent for me to walk home with her. She lived

Cove Hill School, circa 1925. "My father taught there before he became a farmer, and I taught there in 1927 to '28. It was tough. There were 18 to 20 kids and no playground; the kids would just play outside up on the hillside. Hours were 9 to 4, and the term just six months. I taught reading, writing, arithmetic, history, geography, spelling, health, and agriculture. If the kids didn't behave, the parents took care of it and made sure they did!"

in Athens [West Virginia, where the college was located]. But that went on through the summer, and I went back the next summer, '28, and she was still in school. And I spoke to her, and we had some dates that summer.

After I met Opal, I ran out of money and went back to Pocahontas County for my second teaching job. My next school was at my old school, Cove Hill. That's where I went when I was growing up. What I did back in my college days was go to summer school each summer and renew my certificate. You got that first-year certificate renewed, and that was supposed to be a big salary; seventy-five dollars a month. I think the next year's salary at Cove Hill was $77.50 and I was able to save enough to go to school the winter of 1928 at Concord and that gave me enough college credits to be a sophomore.

I went the whole winter term. Opal and I had dates through that winter. And they were not dates like kids have today. You walked home with them and you might have held her hand, or something like that, but that was it. And at nine o'clock, she would tell you, "You've got to get out of here." At nine, if she didn't, her father or her mother walked to the door and said, "It's bedtime, Opal." And I knew what they meant – "Get out of here."

After that 1928-29 term at Concord, I worked in a chemical plant at Belle, West Virginia for the summer—near Charleston right where the DuPont chemical plant sits today—and got just about enough money to go another semester. Instead of going back to college, I taught another year. I taught at the Mount Zion School. I walked from my house in Frost to the Mount Zion School every single day. [It was four miles, up hill and down.] Never missed a day. My students were nice kids, all of them. It was really a good school. We set many of those pines that are around that building. With the summer terms and the winter terms at Concord, I had completed two years of college, which gave me a three-year teaching certificate, which was called a "short normal certificate". Then I went to Frost and taught one year for a salary of eighty dollars a month.

The Best Year of Teaching

My best year of teaching was 1929. I was appointed principal at Frost and I refused to take the job. There was a woman teacher, Miss Hogsett, who taught the lower grades. I went to the superintendent and said, "I won't be principal. I don't want to be principal." He said, "You don't want to teach little kids, do you?" I said, "I'd love to teach little kids." Really, in the back of my mind, I didn't want to be tied down as a principal. I wasn't married yet. I wanted to go to town at night and not be sitting up at all the school programs. He reluctantly gave me the little room and said, "Can you work with a woman?" I said, "I've been listening to my mother up to my age right now. I've been doing what she said." I just laughed. That's a joke not being able to work with women!

When I taught at Frost, there were two rooms, and there were something like seventy five children. They had a pile of kids and no buses or anything. They all walked. There was no busing at that time. I taught first the winter of 1929 to '30. That's the year I taught in the lower grades and Miss Eula Hill was the principal. After that, in 1933, I would return to Frost as the principal and teach for three years in the upper grades; five, six, seven, and eight.

I have never regretted giving up school teaching for doctoring. I liked school teaching and I think that would be my second choice. Having taught in elementary schools, one-room schools, high school, and college, I have had a pretty broad range of experiences. I believe that teaching is one of the most satisfying professions. I think the most satisfying year of teaching was that first year at Frost when I taught grades one, two, three, and four. That is my only year in teaching in which, at the end of the year, I could see the fruits of what I had done. The kids couldn't read or write when they started, and by the end, they could all read and write and spell. I really earned my buck!

I had about twelve first graders. I liked those little kids so much. In fact, in all those years, I can't think of a single kid I disliked. They'd say, "Can we work, can we read, can we do our arithmetic real quick so we can sing? Will you bring your guitar so we can sing at noon or after school?" And I'd take out the guitar and we'd sing! Back then there was no kindergarten. The kids couldn't read, they couldn't write, and most of them couldn't count. When the school year ended, every one of them could stand up and read, and you could ask them to count. They'd count to a thousand or more until you just got tired of listening. They could count by 5s - 5, 10, 15, 20. You could see by the end of school what you had accomplished. In nine years and then ten semesters or more teaching in college, I was never able to see what I had accomplished.

The first thing I taught the child was the child's name and how to write it. Then, "What is your father's name? Write that. What is your mother's name? Write that." They were always really proud when they could do that. "What was your mother's name before she got married? Where do you live?" They all knew that stuff. Then, "What's your post office called? What's the county seat? What's the capital of the state? Who's the governor?" I taught a lot of things that weren't in the book. I used to tell the kids this, "I want you to know this. If someone picked you up and took you away somewhere, how would you get home? You learn these things I tell you and you can go anywhere. You can do anything." They loved that. And they learned that stuff.

A Promissory Note and an Elopement

Then, after my year at Frost I went back to college for the 1930 to '31 term. I had worked on a road construction job building the road from Frost to the Virginia line [current State Route 84] that summer of 1930 and I was finally able to save a little money. I was away from Opal for a year, and we just corresponded a little, and it sort of wore down.

I went back the fall of 1930 as a junior. No chance of any scholarship. No chances of any help whatsoever from your college. And I ran out of money. I told the house mother at the dormitory, "Give up my room at the end of the semester." She told the President, Dr. Marsh, at Concord and Dr. Marsh asked me to come in to the office when I had time. That was about three weeks before the semester ended. I went in his office and he looked at my grades and said, "You don't need to leave. We'll fix it up so you can stay next semester." He got a promissory note out of the drawer, and he wrote the promissory note for $112.50, which I still have somewhere here in my records. "You sign the note and I'll put it here in the safe." The state must have been very sloppy about their collections. "You pay me and I'll give you the note back." So I was able to stay that year. That finished my junior year and I could get a three-year teaching certificate. So I went back to teaching and taught three more years, but I went back to college every summer.

When I went back to school Opal and I had more dates. And I persisted in asking her if she would marry me. And she would just look at me and say, "On what? How would we live?" or put it off. "Are you kidding?"

At the end of that summer in 1931, Opal graduated the eighth day of August with a degree in English and Journalism. And, as she came out of the ceremony, I met her, to congratulate her. And as soon as I finished, she looked at me and said, "Do you still want to get married?" Just like that. She had always treated that very lightly, but looked at me and said, "Do you still want to get married?" I was so flustered that she probably would have turned and walked away. But, anyway, she stared at me, and I said, "Yeah, when?" She said, "Monday." Just like that. Then after it was over, all the shock, I said, "Why Monday?" She said, "You're going home with your friend in Wilco, I'm going home with my aunt in Welch. We can get our license and get married Monday."

Opal in her prime of life.
Just as beautiful as the day Roland first laid eyes on her

She didn't want her parents to know. So, I went home with my friend, and we got married the tenth. That was four years since I first met her.

On Monday we met down in Welch, went to the courthouse, and got our license, and we asked, "Now, is this going to be in the paper?" The clerk said, "No, not likely. We can't keep it out of the paper. This is a public office, but there hasn't been anybody in here in three months to ask about anything."

Opal knew the Methodist minister. We went to his house, got married, and she went back to her aunt's house. We didn't even spend the night in the same house. That's a funny honeymoon! In fact, my friend didn't even know that I had gotten married until after he and I were back at Concord.

On Tuesday my mother-in-law, who managed a little store in Athens that was owned by Ballengee & Whitley, a firm in Beckley, had a salesman to come in who had spent the night in Welch and he laid the Welch paper down on the counter and went off and left it. And, Mrs. Price – that was my mother-in-law – picked the paper up and looked at it. And, on the corner of the front page, it said, "Only one marriage license issued yesterday, Roland P. Sharp and Opal Price." She went wild, I think. She called her husband at the farm crying and going on terrible. And this is what he told me later. "I said, 'Shut up bawling, Essie, and call down there and see if they charged the license to us.' " That was the joke in that. I think he was very glad we got married, but mothers are not so easygoing about their daughters.

Well, anyway, after that, Opal went back home, and I first met her at her home, and the secret was all out - we were married and lived together. I had a school at Mount Zion. She spent part of the winter at her home, part of it she came up and stayed with me. I was living with my parents. She liked my sisters, but she didn't like - She didn't think it was good for us to be living like that. So, she spent part of the winter at home. And the next winter, we really went to housekeeping in Huntersville.

In the fall of 1932, Opal moved to Pocahontas County with me. I went to teach at the Cummings Creek School. Opal and I rented two rooms from Mrs. Sheets. No furniture. We had a King Heater Stove. Mrs. Sheets supplied the bed. We had a two-burner kerosene cook stove, and a one dollar hot plate. And, I believe we had maybe a ninety-eight cent electric percolator. That was our furniture the first year.

Our son Paul was born - Let's see, we were married in August of one year, and in September of the next year, Paul was born. That would be '32. He was born at her home in Athens. She wanted to be down there with her mother. School had started up here. Back then; having a job was really something. We were both afraid that I might lose my job if I took a week or two off. So, she stayed and had Paul, with me up here teaching. Now, when the superintendent heard about that, he came to me and said – when I told him why – he said, "Nobody in their right mind would have objected to that." That's what he told me. Then, of course, she brought him up to Pocahontas County, and we went to Mrs. Sheets'.

That was quite a change for a young lady who was pretty well fixed up at home and had been in college. She was one of two girls in the family. She was the elder, and had been in college - every day she had been in school.

She was just about two weeks under twenty years old when she received her Bachelor's Degree. She was the queen - beauty queen - in the high school. The beauty queens, you know, were voted by the students. That never in any way went to that lady's head. She never—She would look in the glass and say, "I can't see where anybody sees any beauty in this."

I walked to Cummings Creek School. That is the hardest walk I ever had. That road was so muddy that in the winter you had to wear heavy overshoes. By the time you had walked half a mile, you were carrying fifteen pounds of mud!

After Cummings Creek in 1932, I was sent to Frost as principal, and I made one hundred dollars a month. The term

Roland and Opal Sharp's first house in Frost, circa 1933.

was only seven or eight months. When I taught there, I lived across the hill in the little house that Opal and I built. We did practically all the work on that except for ninety dollars that we paid Clarence Curry for some extra work he did. We worked at night for a year. The neighbors helped a little, too. They would stop by on their way somewhere else and nail some nails or dig some dirt while we'd be talking. We built that house in 1933, during really hard times. The total cost of the house was about eight hundred dollars. Our furniture, bed and all, was just seven dollars a month. That compared to now is really nothing. We had no electricity then, but we had a little piano. It cost two dollars a month to rent. We got electricity in 1936 when the Rural Electrification bill passed.

A Degree at Last

Then I gave up one year of teaching to go back to Concord for 1935 to 1936. To finish my degree, I had to take practice teaching. Every degree candidate from those colleges had to take practice teaching. No matter whether you were going to medical school or law school, you had to take practice teaching. By the end of three years I was practically ready to graduate, but I had to take practice teaching because all the colleges in the state required it, regardless of your experience in the classroom. All of the years of teaching experience that I already had counted for nothing! Now those who were graduating in elementary education could take practice teaching in the summer, but I was graduating with a degree in biology. Therefore, my practice teaching had to be in secondary school, and there was no high school in the summertime. I was held back from a degree from 1931 to 1936, just because of practice teaching and because I didn't have the money to go to medical school. You had to have supervised teaching experience of one year, so in 1935, at the end of the semester, I took a leave of absence and took practice teaching at Concord. The superintendent allowed my wife to substitute for me. I graduated in August of 1936. I received the

Bachelor of Science degree in biology at Concord in 1936, but I missed a year of teaching school.

Of course, when I took the leave of absence, I lost out as principal of Frost. They had to put someone else in. I had told the superintendent that I was going to medical school, so it didn't matter where they put me. So I taught at Thorny Creek that year. I went to Thorny Creek's one-room school after I received my Bachelor of Science degree because I received it in the summer term and Thorny Creek was the only school that was left available. It was at the hollow just across the road from where you enter the county high school. I taught at that school in 1936 and 1937, and I walked from Frost to school every day.

I was just happy that I had an eighty-five-dollar-a-month job. The roads through there weren't gravel. You had to plod through the mud daily. Then we didn't go to school at nine o'clock and leave at two-thirty or three o'clock. We got to school at about eight-thirty in the morning and we were in school until four o'clock or sometimes until after that. Teachers then were so afraid for their jobs. If you had a teaching job then, you were really "in the in," and nobody wanted to be caught away from the school five minutes before four o'clock because that was enough of an infraction to lose your job.

Then, after I taught at that school, they had an opening at Green Bank High School and I was sent there. I taught there one year and then I went to the medical school in Morgantown at West Virginia University in 1938.

I was telling someone the other day; I never felt that I was being imposed on even though I didn't make much money teaching. I felt so lucky to have a job! The most I ever made teaching school was $110 a month. I made $110 at Green Bank High School for a year and I made $100 a month as a principal at Frost.

My year at Green Bank they gave me four subjects; sociology one semester, economics the next semester, civics to the freshmen, and geography. And my degree was in biology and chemistry! But the attitude was, "Well, you taught in elementary school, so you ought to know enough about these subjects to teach them." And the other teachers threw up their hands and said, "I haven't taught elementary school. I don't know any civics, I don't know any economics, and I don't know any geography." And my attitude was sort of, "Where were you when you were going to school?" Civics and geography were required in seventh and eighth grade then, so I had taught them, and I was surprised to find that my freshmen and sophomores barely knew what county they lived in!

After two years, one at Thorny Creek and one at Green Bank, nothing had changed about my financial situation, which was that I still didn't have the money to go to medical school. I applied to West Virginia University Medical School and got in, but I had only enough money for one semester. My wife said, "Take a shot. Now or never. I'll do what I can." I told you, I think, that married women were not often employed back then. They could hardly be employed for anything. She worked Christmas holidays at Montgomery Ward in Morgantown, and then she got a substitute-teaching job in Pocahontas County at Droop Mountain because no one would take that job. They had a controversy there about moving the kids to a school down in the valley, and the superintendent said, "I don't believe anybody born in Pocahontas County can settle those people down!"

Opal Saves the Day

When Opal came to Pocahontas County as my wife in 1932, she couldn't get a job. She had never had a teaching job, a full-time teaching job, so she could only substitute because no county would hire a married woman. Jobs were so scarce, and she substituted some in this county, but very little. Then Superintendent Eric Clutter called us. He knew us both well and knew she was really a good English teacher—not only a good English teacher, but could really keep order in the classroom and was very diplomatic with parents. He called her and asked her if she would go out on Droop Mountain and take that school.

That year [1938], the School Board had closed the Droop Mountain School and sent the students to Hillsboro. Those people would not send their kids to Hillsboro and the Board took them to court and tried to fine them or even put them in jail. The families just said, "We're not going to send them to Hillsboro. We're going to keep our school!" The court got tired of that and finally told the Board of Education, "Go ahead and open the school. These kids haven't had school from the last of October or first of November, whenever school started back then, until the New Year. Nobody has sent a kid to Hillsboro yet, and we're still bringing them into court." So Mr. Clutter said to Opal, "We're going to have school. Will you go out there and teach that school? We don't know of anyone we can send out there." She came immediately and boarded with Mr. Bruffey at the foot of Droop Mountain, the big white house on the left just as you start up. Mr. Bruffey was the school bus driver. She'd ride up with him in the morning and he'd pick up the high school students and then take her out to the school.

The first day that she was there, every parent came to that school and sat down with her and said, "Now, Mrs. Sharp, was you sent up here as a tool of that Board of Education or did you come here to teach our kids? Are you working with them to get us down to Hillsboro?" She said, "I came up here to teach these kids all I can teach them from now until the school term ends. What you do after that I have no control over, but I came to teach your kids." They responded so positively. "Okay, we'll help anyway we can."

She said it was the best bunch of parents she ever taught for. They came to school to help with everything. They helped her clean up the schoolhouse. They came out there every single day to see if they could do something. She got along very well with them and she taught those kids just about as much as she herself knew. Those parents, the ones I knew later after she taught there, said, "Your wife taught our kids more than if we had started them last fall."

And from then on, of course, Mr. Clutter knew her well. He knew she was a good teacher and he would have her at Green Bank when they needed a substitute teacher, but they didn't need substitutes very often. I taught there in 1937–38. That was my next to the last year of teaching. The way we got enough for me to pay the school tuition was she taught part-time during the winter of 1936–37. She was called only a substitute teacher, but the teacher who taught there was sick all winter. Mr. Clutter kept calling her, and Mr. McMillan, the principal, liked her and knew she was a good English teacher. She had a degree in English and journalism. She was a really good English teacher. But I'm getting ahead of myself.

Leaving Teaching

I did not miss teaching children when I went to medical school, except for that year with the little kids, because when you're teaching in medical school, students were waiting for every word that came out of your mouth. Medical school isn't a casual experience. It is a coveted opportunity. You get it or you get out. Students knew that there was someone else just waiting for their place. You had no trouble with discipline or anything like that. Everybody is in class all of the time. They want more than you can give them.

As teaching in the one-room schools went on, there got to be political problems. After I left teaching in the county, officials began to have discipline problems with the children and other political problems with people in the community. For example, this child over here takes home a C, but the parents aren't used to their child bringing home a C, even though their child is a C student. If the parents were prominent in the community, you had to just put up with all of that.

Back in the early part of this century there were something like one hundred one-room schools in the county with everybody teaching something different. My dad was a teacher in a one-room school in the early part of the century and he could tell me a lot about it. Some of the kids coming out of those one-room schools could have gone on to college, while others could barely read. It just depended on what kind of a teacher they had.

Well, all of that got standardized by Mr. C.E. Flynn when he became superintendent. He had meeting after meeting with teachers and citizens, year after year. In his day, until 1932, the county superintendent of schools was elected, just like the sheriff and the assessor. Mr. Flynn served a couple of elected terms, then after 1932, he was appointed for several more terms. Then he was politically removed from his position and Mr. Clutter was moved in. Teaching is political because people are anxious for certain jobs. The only way they can get them is pulling political strings.

One of the reasons that I gave up teaching and moved on was that there were no good jobs in the county. When I was accepted at Morgantown, I was teaching at Green Bank. I didn't want to give up the teaching job and just let loose, even though my wife had said, "Go for it!" I went to the superintendent, Mr. Eric Clutter at that time, who had taught me math at the high school. I said, "Mr. Clutter, I want to go to medical school this fall, and I have been accepted. Will you give me a leave of absence, because I may flunk out? I really don't know. And I don't know how long it's going to take me. If I could have a leave of absence I would feel a little bit better psychologically." And he said, "Sure, that's no problem."

I think he sort of liked me for being his student anyway. He said, "Tell me why you're teaching up at Green Bank. I said, "Mr. Clutter, this is the reason. There are four or five good paying jobs in this county. the principal of Green Bank High School, the principal of Marlinton High School, the principal of Marlinton Grade School, and your job. I'm a Republican, and I know that I'll never get any of those. I think I am worth more than 110 dollars a month!" And he laughed real big, and he said, "Go on, go on. You'll have the leave." He gave me a leave of absence to go to Morgantown. Then, he gave me a leave of absence every year that I was in Kirksville, Missouri in medical school, years later, even though I didn't request it.

Those were the best years of my life even if I didn't earn any money!

What I Took Away from Teaching

I attribute a lot of my knowledge to the fact that I taught school. I learned a lot about human nature from being with the kids and talking with them and their parents. I was one who really mixed with the community everywhere I taught. I played the guitar and the piano, and we had programs all the time. I was a good barber and did that to get part of my way through college. I couldn't do that in medical school, though. I didn't have time. I cut every kid's hair and my mother told me, "Don't you dare do that. Somebody will come in and tell you, 'I can take care of my own kids.'" She was leery when I took clippers to school. The kids were all shabby. I cut their hair—all of them. In every one-room school I had the best-groomed bunch of kids there. They could sing, put on programs, speak in public—everything like that. I went back and told my mom, "You were 100 percent wrong. You know what happened? Their parents came at noon and said, 'Would you cut my hair?'" I was cutting the parents' hair out on Cummings Creek and up at Wesley Chapel!

I am one that has been very much against the massive school consolidation in education. It destroyed the community. When I was up there, Frost was a real tightly knit community. They had good church attendance. All those kids went to church. You had a program in the fall, Armistice Day. You had another program at Thanksgiving and one at Christmas. You had a Valentine's Day program and you had an Easter Program, and every one of those parents was sitting right there, clapping their hands. They were proud of their kids. When they moved the schools out of the communities, the feeling was, "So what?" Parents didn't go to their kids' schools anymore, only to the school maybe at graduation. Soon thereafter, church participation fell off as well.

The Path Through Medical School

1938–1944

"The osteopathic school of medicine [taught] that it is a privilege to be a doctor, not your right. It is a privilege. It is your duty to see everybody who comes in your office, whether they pay you or they do not."

—Roland Sharp

I finished my two-year pre-med coursework, which is what it was called, back in 1931, but I didn't graduate from college until 1936. After that, I continued teaching school until I was admitted into medical school at West Virginia University [WVU] in 1938. If I had had the money to go to medical school in 1931, the year I completed my pre-med, I probably would have flunked out. But by 1938, I was a more serious student with responsibilities. I was married and had a six-year-old boy and everything depended on that. I could sit down and read a book! When I finished my pre-med course in 1931, all I wanted to do was go to fraternity parties on the weekend. I could dance. Fortunately I learned to do that in high school! If you could dance or play a musical instrument, partying is what the first two years of college were for you. After I got married and started earning a living, medical school became something serious. I forgot about all that other stuff.

I'd considered being a doctor from the time I was in high school, but I was in college during the Depression and there didn't appear to be any chance that I could get to medical school. However, when I went to college, I majored in biology. Biology was a pre-med course of study and I think I had that in the back of my mind. After I had completed the bachelor's degree, I began to consider medical school because teaching was such an unstable job. The pay was poor, and you weren't sure if you were going to get paid during the Depression. I considered medical school more seriously as the days went by.

I was thirty years old when I started medical school. Going to school was real business, particularly when you were teaching at the same time. I was teaching a class of fifty young students who wanted to be doctors, many of whom had already graduated from college. So when you got up before a class of college graduates, you just didn't feel nearly as comfortable as you did in a little one-room school at Frost. But I think it just turned out to be a blessing that I started medical school so late.

Money for Medical School

I had been invited up to Morgantown [WV} to the [WVU] medical school for an interview sometime in March or April of '38 and it wasn't like medical school admissions are today. They interviewed me and before I left that day, they said, "You're in." That's it. Today, they have a lengthy admission process and then they put you on a waiting list and try to make it as stressful as possible.

Anyway, my wife and I had built this little house. When I got admission to medical school, I still owed a little bit on the house we had built, maybe $600. I went to Mr. John Sydenstricker, who was president of First National Bank in Marlinton and I said, "Mr. Sydenstricker, I have been admitted to medical school in Morgantown this fall, and I've come in here for two things. I don't have much money saved up. I came in here first to see whether I might be able to get fifty dollars or something like that occasionally, if I get in a pinch. The second thing I came in here to ask was whether you would let me pay just the interest on my house loan here until I get out of school."

Mr. Sydenstricker told me I was out of my head. He went right up through the ceiling. He looked at me and said, "Any man your age who has a good job teaching in this county and is well-respected has no business going out on a wild goose chase."

That's what he called it. He said, "I won't loan you anything and you better pay your note in full before you go, because we're going to collect it."

He wrote me a letter, which I may still have to this day. It may take me a couple of days to hunt it up. He told me it was his experience that men who did stupid tricks like this ended up amounting to nothing. They would loan me nothing. I hadn't really asked for a loan. I had gotten a little loan for the material to build the house and all I had asked was for him to let me pay the interest on that while I went to medical school. He said, "We will not under any consideration allow you to do that." That was the best thing that ever happened to me, because every time medical school was hard—and without money it was very hard—I had the incentive to prove him wrong. He talked to me [at the bank] and then when I got home, he sat down and wrote me that letter. My father-in-law was furious and said, "I'll just give him a check for that amount."

Well, there was no way that Mr. Sydenstricker at the First National Bank was going to loan me any money. So then I went over and talked to Dr. Jim Price who was the president of another bank in town. Dr. Price was an optimist. He said, "Now, there are no formal arrangements to make loans to students, but if you run short, you come up here to me." I did two or three times and he would write me a little note and say, "Take this down to the bank," where they would give me a deposit slip—he was financing it himself. He always used pencils about three inches long. You have probably heard people talk about how tight he was with money. I never saw him have even a whole pencil in his office. Even when you went to see him as a doctor, he gave you your pills in the envelopes people had used to make their bank deposits. He never gave you your medicine in a drug envelope. Now that's recycling!

Dr. Price looked at the catalogue and saw all the anatomy and physiology and said, "Go. You'll learn all the rest through

Roland Sharp's son and his in-laws, Essie Keatley and John H. Price of Athens, WV, at a cabin in Seneca State Park, circa 1937. "That's the man who paid the bank so that I could go to school."

practice." He said, "You go right on to medical school and if you can afford for your wife to go, you take her too." Well, we didn't think we could afford it, but I took heart at that. Opal should have gone to medical school. She was as good a doctor as I was before she died. She could diagnose a thyroid problem before I could do a lab test.

All through medical school, I had so little money that it was sort of a shock when I finally started working. I've told people this a lot of times. When I graduated from medical school and went to work as a coal company doctor, they paid us in cash. They paid me in cash for the seventeen years I worked there. You went to the window at the coal company office, you signed your name, and the payroll clerk checked it and gave you your cash. I remember my first pay envelope had seven hundred-dollar bills and a two-dollar bill. I had never had my hands on a hundred-dollar bill—I'd never seen one! I've said for years since then that I shut up the office, went straight home, and my wife and I looked at those hundred-dollar bills the rest of the day. That's not strictly true, but it really tells how I felt! I made more in one payday than I'd made in any year of teaching for ten years!

After I got through medical school I would stop in and see old Mr. Sydenstricker, and I never forgot when he told me going to medical school was just a crazy idea. When I got the job with the coal company after medical school, you could still buy Series E war bonds. I would take my pay envelope up to Mr. Sydenstricker. I wouldn't buy an E-bond from anyone else. I always asked for Mr. Sydenstricker and I gave him that envelope. He'd look at the envelope, and he'd lay it down, write on it, pick up the envelope, and look at it—because I'm sure that two weeks of my pay was twice as much as his month's pay! They started me at $25,000, which after getting seventy five or one hundred dollars a month [as a school teacher] was absolutely astonishing. What I should have said was, "Here I am, Mr. Sydenstricker. Well, I went on that goose chase, and I caught the goose!"

Medical School in Morgantown

There were no government loans for medical students back then. There was no bank that would loan you a nickel. You had to afford to go yourself or have a wife who would send you. You could not support a family. I was married and had a little boy, but I had a wife who was as much committed to my going to school as I was. Opal said to me, "I'll work at anything." She had a degree in English and journalism, but married teachers were not hired any time during the Depression. She graduated in 1931 and we were married. There was no chance of her getting a job after that, but I had a job teaching then. I kept waiting and waiting for the Depression to end so she might get a job or I could get a job in the summers or something so I could afford to go to medical school. It just never happened though.

So I was teaching at Green Bank High School and applied to medical school. I was accepted and tuition was only one hundred dollars. So Opal's answer was, "If you're ever gonna do it, let's get with it. I'll work at anything." When I went to Morgantown to the WVU School of Medicine, Opal went up with me. Our son [Roland P. [Paul] Sharp, Jr.] stayed with my parents here at Frost. He started school the year that I started medical school.

Opal and I had an apartment that we shared with my cousin and three other boys. One was a medical student, one was an engineering student, one was a pre-med student, and the other one was Harry Scoffield, my mother's sister Clara's son, who started to pharmacy school when I started to medical school. We took a lot of food to eat [from home in Frost] and the apartment had bedrooms enough to take care of the whole group of us. Opal knew two of the other boys. She knew my cousin and she knew Tom Nunnley, the medical student who was to be my lab partner.

When we went to Morgantown, Paul went with us part of the time. But most of the time, he wanted to stay with my parents. He had no children to play with up there, and here he

Roland Sharp's parents Aaron and Odessa (Dessa) Sharp at their home in Frost, with Roland and Opal's three-year-old son Paul (Roland P. Sharp, Jr.), in 1935.

Roland Sharp in his anatomy lab coat during his first year of medical school at WVU, 1938, in his neighborhood on McClain Avenue in Morgantown.

had cousins and neighbors. He started school at Frost that year, in the two room school where I had taught.

Opal said she would go along and cook our supper, and she did until the end of the year. When she could, she worked at Montgomery Ward for fifteen cents an hour. But it didn't take anything to live. When she went back to Pocahontas County in January, she was only back there about a week or two when Mr. Clutter, the Superintendent of Schools, called her and asked her if she would substitute teach. Substitute teaching gave her enough money to get by on and when she wasn't there, the four other boys and I rented an apartment for twenty four dollars that would sleep six people. We each put five dollars a month in a pot to buy groceries, and we usually got by on that.

Now, when Opal was substituting, Paul stayed with my mother and father at Frost. They were elderly, and Paul liked them, just as they were. They lived close to us, and he would stay with them just as freely as he would stay with us. And he did not call my mother "grandma," he called my mother "Mommy". And he called my dad, Mr. Aaron. My dad's name was Aaron Sharp, but so many of the people in the community had gone to school to him. He taught six or eight years. They called him Mr. Aaron. And my son, his grandson, always, till he died, called him Mr. Aaron, not grandfather. .Paul called his real mother, Opal, "Opal," and he called me "Roland" because that's what my parents called me.

Opal and I first got to Morgantown in time for me to go to summer school at WVU in 1938. I wanted to take refresher courses in some subjects I felt I needed to brush up on. I took a couple of graduate courses. In the fall of 1938, I started to medical school, but I was smart. I had been teaching long enough that I was looking at all the angles. I noticed when I was looking at the medical school course catalog that it was all graduate school numbers. So I went to the graduate school committee and said, "These are all graduate school numbers.

Roland and Opal Sharp dressed for a party at West Virginia University, during his year of medical school there, 1938–39.

Will they count on a degree?" And they said, "Sure." At that time, certain courses that were required for a zoology master's degree, like two courses in genetics, counted towards a master's degree and a [medical] doctor's degree both. At the end of the first year, I stayed in Morgantown for the summer term of 1939 and took fourteen more graduate hours—all A's. By then, I had more than enough credits for the master's degree in zoology. I am listed in the 1940 graduate class at Morgantown. If I didn't get through medical school, I would at least have a better salary for teaching.

Since I [now] had a master's degree, the biology department at WVU offered me a fellowship for the following year. They gave me a job at Morgantown for fifty dollars a month to teach one course. The biology department chair told me, "Your business will be to do one lecture in freshman biology."

I went down to the medical school and I said, "I'm going to have to be a part-time student because I'm going to have to teach one class."

The dean and the committee of the medical school said, "No way. We don't take part-time students." And I knew two or three part-time students, so naturally I brought all of that up. "Well," they said, "Circumstances have changed." Later the dean at the medical school at Morgantown told me the reason they couldn't admit part-timers was because of accrediting problems. The committee that accredited the medical school had put them on probation, but he was not free to tell anyone. If it had become public that they were under probation, nobody would apply to the school. Until you've graduated from an accredited medical school, you cannot be licensed. At that time only four states would license you if you had graduated from an unaccredited medical school. All of the other forty four required that you be graduated from an accredited school before you could even be admitted to take the medical boards. So WVU could no longer take a part-time student.

So I had to give up that fellowship that paid fifty dollars a month and I was really upset that year - no fellowship, and no money for medical school. I lost a year and went back to Pocahontas County to teach at Wesley Chapel School.

My professors all stuck with me through that year. My biochemistry professor from Morgantown who I audited the class with called me up on the last day of lecture and he wrote in my laboratory manual, "You are the only student who has ever audited one of my classes who has never missed a day." And he autographed it. When I started talking about going to Kirksville College of Osteopathic Medicine, he told me he could guarantee me a three-year scholarship at the University of Rochester, where he'd earned his biochemistry degree, if I wanted to go on for a Ph.D. He urged me to go on for a Ph.D. "Why would they want me?" I asked. He said, "I see you're the kind who when you start something, you're consistent and steadfast—which is what research needs." He said, "As a doctor you'll never know anything. If you go on in zoology, you'll know something. If you're a doctor, you won't know biochemistry, you won't know zoology, you won't know anything." He was really hard on doctors. He was saying that I wouldn't have a lot of expertise in any one area. "So if I were you, that's what I'd worry about instead of going on to the second year of med school."

Even though I had to give up on medical school at WVU, my idea in getting my master's degree was still to be able to get a teaching assistantship in a medical school somewhere. If you had a master's degree, a lot of medical schools would, if they had openings, pay your tuition and a small salary for you to serve as a graduate assistant. My graduate instructors at Morgantown were good friends as well as instructors, and they gave me names of places to write. I spent that year writing letters to medical schools asking for instructorships. Students at the medical school at WVU gave me catalogs for dozens of schools. At the graduate school at the university, instructors recommended me to a lot of medical schools. I was flat broke. I had no money. There were no loans. Bankers wouldn't talk to you about loans. That was one of the effects of the Depression. My relatives who had any money wouldn't even talk to me. They'd move to get away from me if they thought I was looking for money for medical school. I looked and I looked, but there was nothing open. Two or three of my professors at Morgantown gave me really good advice. They said, "There are schools of osteopathic medicine and most of them are increasing in size and increasing their faculty. You might have a chance."

Anyway I cast around the country to all different medical schools. And right at the last minute in 1940 I got a telegram from the medical school in Kirksville, Missouri. Opal brought the telegram to the Pocahontas County Fair where I was working in a concession with Dr. McCutcheon's son. Clark McCutcheon and I were selling beer and hot dogs. It said something to the following effect; "We have your application in the file, and I'm the new dean. The dean you wrote to has retired as of July the first. I am the new dean. [The application had been on file for six months or a year.] Are you still available? Our histologist has taken a semester leave of absence. Would you be available for a semester?" You never telephoned then, in 1940. He said, "Wire me back. Wire collect."

So I wired back and said I was qualified and would be willing to take the job. I got [a wire] back within a few hours asking if I could come out for an interview. *Wire collect.* Thank goodness the school was saying wire collect, because I didn't even have the money to pay the telegram fee. I wired him back that I could not come for an interview, but I would come one week early and if I did not qualify, I'd return to West Virginia to my teaching. If I'd had the money to go out there to Missouri for an interview I would have used it to go back to Morgantown!

I was then assigned to Dunmore as principal for the next school year in Pocahontas County, but the dean in Kirksville wired me back that it would be satisfactory if I arrived a week early. I packed my bags, said goodbye to Opal and my little boy and I was on the road.

I left I believe the third of September. Then there were buses from Clarksburg to Bluefield that came through Marlinton each day in both directions. I caught the Greyhound bus in Lewisburg at nine o'clock in the morning and got off at seven o'clock the next evening in Kirksville, Missouri. Kirksville was right at the Missouri-Iowa border.

More young people were drafted, or enlisted, and there was a vacancy at Green Bank High School and Opal was put in the English Department, and she taught two years after I went to Missouri. And at that time, Paul rode to school with her, and enrolled in Green Bank, instead of staying with my parents.

It wasn't too hard being apart for two years. We were both so busy. And, listen, when finances were tough during the Depression, nobody objected to staying apart. If they had two days work, you didn't even discuss something like that. It was, "I could work."

When she came out to Missouri in the summertime, she took a course that the school gave for doctor's wives that wanted to work in the office in what was called "Clinical Technology". They taught them how to do blood counts, how to do red cells, white cells, how to do urinalysis, how to take blood pressure, how to draw blood, just general things, but it was called- Seems to me it was clinical pathology or clinical technology. It was something like a three months course. But any doctor's wife, who thought she might work in the doctor's office, did that.

Starting at Kirksville College of Osteopathic Medicine

I didn't enter as a medical student until the second semester at Kirksville. The first semester I didn't enter because I didn't have tuition and I didn't know how long I would be staying. Besides, I had the first year of courses from Morgantown.

The histologist and embryologist who was taking a leave of absence had been there for a good many years. Well, his daughters had married doctors and moved to Ohio, and he took a leave of absence to see if he and his wife should follow their family. At the end of the semester he resigned.

The dean called me in at the end of the first semester and said, "I have good news. Dr. Green resigned. You are the histology-embryology instructor from now on. You have a permanent job. Would you like to go to school?" And I said, "Yes, I would, but I don't have any money to pay the tuition." Their tuition was $240, but I didn't have that. If I had had even $100, I would've just stayed at Morgantown. He said, "Don't worry about that. Well, I think you've done a good job so far, and I have the right to waive the tuition of one or two students. If you are interested, I will waive tuition for you. You're not getting paid enough anyway." And I said, "Great! I'll just go to school."

The dean told me, "If you want to transfer your credits here, we'll give you hour-for-hour credit. We'll not give you credit for time. You'll have to have four years in this institution because this institution is fully accredited, but not by the same accrediting agency as WVU. We're both accredited, but it's accredited by one organization and we're by another." Luckily, I had to take only three [years] because the war came along and you graduated in three years of twelve months instead of four years of nine months. So I graduated in the same amount of time as I would have if I had stayed in Morgantown.

I had had all my first-year classes in Morgantown, but at Kirksville they were teaching their anatomy students in their first year far more than I had learned at WVU. The first year of anatomy was a lecture demonstration and the second year was dissection. Those students who had had the first year of anatomy were far sharper than I was in anatomy. Fortunately I didn't have to teach any anatomy! I had a whole lot of histology, or microscopic anatomy, and I had had graduate courses in that before I went to medical school.

So the first thing I told the dean was, "I don't think I can keep up with your students in anatomy." He said, "We can solve that easily. You go down to the laboratory at night. The prosectors are dissecting the body for their demonstrations the next day." The prosectors dissected a certain part of the arm or whatever and the next day they wheeled the cadaver into the amphitheater where the professor lectured on that dissection. The prosector helped with the visual identification of parts on the cadaver. So I went at night and watched the prosectors and I said, "I'd be a little embarrassed to go down there." The dean said, "Oh, don't worry about that. They'll think you're supervising it. You're a faculty member. Don't say anything, just sit there and watch." And that's exactly what I did.

I did the same thing in biochemistry. The biochemistry they had taught at Morgantown was the graduate school biochemistry, not medical school biochemistry. It didn't even resemble medical school biochemistry, but that's what they were getting at Morgantown. You got it in the department of chemistry. I had audited the biochemistry course at Morgantown that they were giving to home economics and agriculture students, and when I got out there to Kirksville and went to class, I was really surprised. At the end of the semester of the second year they always gave reviews, and the dean told me, "If you don't think you know enough biochemistry, you go to the reviews every day—just sit in on them."

Osteopathic Education: A Difference in Philosophy

So I happened to go to the institution in Missouri. I liked the place. I liked the school. I liked the people. It was an osteopathic school. Morgantown was a straight medical school. Osteopathic medical schools seemed so different. At Morgantown, instructors didn't talk to you. They just lectured to you and when you left class that was it. Most whom you met out in the hall said nothing—just walked past you. You were a student. When I went to Kirksville, I met the instructors. The instructors were talking to the students in the hall. They knew their first names and they talked about classes. At Morgantown in chemistry you'd learn formulas, but at Kirksville you learned chemistry as it related to diseases.

When you went to class at Morgantown, in the first lecture I heard "There are thirty of you all today. At the end of this semester there'll be only twenty five. At the end of the year, it could be as low as twenty, because we're only prepared to take care of twenty next year." When I went to Kirksville, the professor said, "We've taken fifty students. We have fifty places. We can take fifty students in our second year. If you do not reach the second year, your background will be poor, your attitude toward your studies will be poor, or you will just be plain no good. In other words, we're prepared to take care of every one of you who comes in here if you are dedicated students and you show a social attitude to take care of patients. Today you became our colleagues. Come to us anytime you want any help. If it's in class, out of class, if you need tutoring or if you feel that you're poorly trained in one field in your pre-med, tell us so we can give you help."

That was the main difference. The straight medical colleges, as I saw it, were operating a planned scarcity program. They wanted as few doctors as possible so the income of the doctor would be as great as possible. The osteopathic school of medicine did not emphasize income in any way. Their attitude was that it is a privilege to be a doctor, not your right. It is a privilege. It is your duty to see everybody who comes in your office, whether they pay you or they do not. If there is an indigent person in your community, it is your social duty, not only your social but your Christian or spiritual duty, to see that that person is taken care of. That's the difference in teaching. That's what impressed me. They taught the body, the mind, and the soul. These days every medical school is doing that.

When I went there, my idea was to go there and as my instructors back in West Virginia said, "Go there and get a year or two of experience as an instructor. Then you might be able to go to any university you want for the rest of your education as a graduate instructor. Experience is what will count to get your education." Well, Kirksville gave me experience and a valuable philosophy. When I finished that year, I didn't want to leave.

I didn't tell you the best part. I started as an instructor in histology, but after three or four semesters of that they moved me on up into another department. By mid-1942, I had completed the whole four years of the curriculum, but I still hadn't fulfilled the hours-in-residence time requirement. I was qualified to teach in any department because I had the academic credit. They moved me to pathology. That's how I became eligible for certification in pathology. When I left the school in Kirksville, I was Acting Chairman of Pathology. I was listed in the catalogue as Assistant Professor of Anatomy by the time I was into my senior year because I had completed the four years of medical school. All I lacked was the hours-in-residence, not curriculum hours.

When I graduated from medical school, Dr. Morris Thompson, the acting president, offered me $350 a month to stay on there as a faculty member and he said, "That is more than I make." Years later, when we started the medical school here in Lewisburg, he was one of our first speakers for the convocation and in his speech he told that story. I didn't think he'd ever remember that!

World War II Erupts

I was at Kirksville in my second year of medical school when the Japanese bombed Pearl Harbor. I was lecturing in histology, conducting a laboratory, and taking classes. We woke up one morning and found out that we were at war. We all - the whole class listened to President Roosevelt tell about the bombing and that we were at war with Japan. Very shortly after that, gasoline was rationed. You couldn't buy an automobile. There were so many products that you couldn't buy, and everybody had to register for the draft, which I had already done. I believe the draft started about 1940. Back then, your county draft board classified you. They started calling so many per month until

On Kirksville Faculty

DR. ROLAND SHARP

Dr. Sharp has been appointed Assistant Professor in Pathology at the Kirksville College of Osteopathy and Surgery. He was graduated from K.C.O.S. in December, 1943. Before entering the study of osteopathy Dr. Sharp had earned his A.B. degree at Concord State College, majoring in biology and social science; and his M.S. degree from West Virginia University, taking his work in zoology. During his undergraduate studies he was a member of Chi Beta Phi, national honorary undergraduate science fraternity. He is a member of the West Virginia Academy of Science. He is a member of Phi Sigma Gamma and was active in school affairs while a student at Kirksville.

A 1944 article in the Journal of Osteopathy on Dr. Sharp's promotion to assistant professor at Kirksville.

I think we had ten million people in service when the war ended—both men and women.

I think the reaction toward the announcement about Pearl Harbor was, "It's a terrible thing." There was no TV to see it on, so we just heard the president's speech on the radio. Probably twenty-five percent of people heard the president speak, because at that time, I don't believe that many people were listening to the radio. They listened to radio at certain times, maybe for the news and their special program, but people weren't addicted to radio like they are to TV today. We were shocked, but it took a month to really get the pictures of it in magazines and newspapers. It took at least that long to absorb the shock of what a calamity it actually was.

Now with the war, remember that people had just been talking about peace for years and that didn't change until 1939, when World War II really started in Europe. Hitler overran Poland. We talked about it a lot, and a lot of young men who weren't employed joined the Air Force or the Navy. In 1938, '39, and '40 there was a big push to join the Army or the Navy because there was no work and they offered to train you. At least the young people could make some money that way and get some training. After 1944 they also offered that if you joined the services, your college would be paid for when you came out, and that's what brought the big influx of students into college after the war ended. The colleges were just flooded with students. It was so different from when I started. After the war every student you met was being financed by one of the services. Then, banks began advertising loans to students because the government stood good for them. Unfortunately, the government ended up paying off those loans for those who never got jobs.

We didn't really know about the Nazis until the war began in '39. We just considered them a political party, that's all. It was not until after the war started and the Americans and the British became involved that we learned what was really happening in concentration camps in Germany. I didn't know about those camps until the war was half over. You heard about it, but you didn't know how much was propaganda or media hype, or if the media was just making big stories out of something that seemed possible. But when the British and American troops invaded Europe, after Normandy, then they found out what was going on as they liberated camps. That is when all of our publications were full of accounts of exactly what had gone on. I was very surprised by the camps when they came to light, because Germany was considered a civilized, peaceable country. The German public probably was. When you get a person like Hitler who was a fanatic and who had enormous charisma as a leader, anything can happen, I guess.

I am amazed at the things that Hitler did that the medical profession sanctioned. Germany was at one time a leader in medicine. If you were trained in this country, you went to Germany for postgraduate education. That was considered a real privilege. Hitler had medical men doing experiments that you wouldn't even do on animals. He attempted to breed what he called the "Superior Race." They had to be blue-eyed. I understand that most of the blond women, married or single, were crossbred like we do with cattle in this country. They were mated with blond Norwegian-type soldiers. A grandson of mine spent a month in Germany as an exchange student with a family that told him a lot about that. There were hundreds of thousands of German young people who knew only their mother. They didn't know the paternal side at all. I don't know why the medical community in Germany sanctioned that. I don't know whether they were afraid or what.

German doctors performed any and every experiment on those people they had in the concentration camps. They tried all of their vaccines on them and they experimented with extensive brain surgeries. They tried any type of injection, intravenous or intramuscular. I really can't conceive of that myself. But they say that if you get a fanatic leader with charisma and military force behind him, he can persuade the masses do the unthinkable.

I'm not an extreme religious person, but you can't have a great medical profession unless you're guided by religious practice. The Ten Commandments are the roadmap to civilization and most religions encompass them. If your religion does not encompass those precepts, you won't have a civilization.

It's hard to believe that six million people were executed in a country of that size. That was the worst thing Hitler did. His hatred toward all races except northern Europeans overwhelmed what people should have remembered from their religious education. That also eliminated many of the best scientific brains from Germany. He executed them, or they escaped to Russia or the United States.

The war didn't change the medical school curriculum here in the United States, but it changed the number of students coming in. You had far fewer applicants for your classes. Medical schools changed from two semesters to continuous operation. Liberal arts colleges operated just the same as they always had. Medical school became a year-round enterprise. When a semester ended and graduation took place over the weekend, the next semester started the following Monday. Med schools were taking applicants year-round instead of the way they do now. During the war the problem was to get a class of really qualified students, because half of your qualified students were enlisting in service. They'd just drop out of college and enlist in the army, navy, or marines. I would have liked to have enlisted, because both of my brothers and my cousins were in the war and I felt a little bit guilty by not doing it, but the institution [the osteopathic school] and the draft board would not permit me to do that. In other words they informed me, "You are in a job, a position, necessary for the war." So I was right there until the war dwindled down.

When the United States entered World War II, jobs became plentiful everywhere. Back in Pocahontas County, after so many men were drafted, they finally hired my wife as a full-time teacher, but it didn't do me much good then financially because I was already in Missouri at medical school and had a teaching assistantship that supported both of us. She stayed in Pocahontas County that winter and half of the next winter. Then she came with me to Missouri because she was offered a job out there teaching in a country school for one year.

My wife and son came to live with me in 1942 and stayed until I was through. When Opal came to Missouri, Paul came to Missouri with her. He had her in school out there, and he graduated from the sixth grade when I got my degree. And they stayed out there with me until I left in the fall of 1944. It was pretty hard to be out in Kirksville without my family. However, over the years I had gone to school away from Opal at times because she got her degree in 1931 and I didn't get mine until five years later because I was teaching school and going to Concord in the summer terms.

After she spent her first year teaching in that one-room school, Northeast Missouri State Teacher's College [today's Truman University], which was in Kirksville, hired her as an instructor in remedial reading. They were impressed with Opal's credentials. This ended our financial difficulties.

The Teaching Hospitals and the Nursing Home

Kirksville had two hospitals and we were trained there and in a nursing home. One was called The College Hospital, the American School of Osteopathy. It was built in 1903 and had 110 beds, making it one of the biggest hospitals in the region outside of Kansas City and St. Louis. The one across the street was the Laughlin Hospital. It was owned by the Laughlins and that's where they did all the acute surgery. They did deliveries and one thing and another in the other hospital, but all of the really acute, serious surgery went on in the Laughlin Hospital because the old gentleman, George Laughlin, was one of the America's first orthopedic surgeons. He was supposed to be the first orthopedic surgeon to pin a fractured hip, which he did with a twenty-penny nail. He drilled a hole and drove in a twenty-penny nail. He is in a lot of scientific journals as the one who did that. Dr. George Laughlin was the president of the Kirksville School of Osteopathic Medicine and his wife was the daughter of Andrew Taylor Still, the founder of osteopathic medicine. Dr. Laughlin was the orthopedic surgeon, and his son was one of the general surgeons at that hospital.

The school had a surgical amphitheater with maybe a hundred seats around it, like a silo. Every time there was an OB, they called everyone in the class; "OB in the pit!" They took attendance! I must have seen a hundred or two deliveries before I left.

The Kirksville school started a nursing home. They weren't called nursing homes before then. They were just called "homes for poor people" or "infirmaries." The school bought an old hotel and started putting in the indigent patients, those who had no parents, and the old ones who had no relatives. Patients who had terminal cancer and those with multiple sclerosis were very common in the Mississippi Valley area. It was years before I saw a case of multiple sclerosis in West Virginia. Rocky Mountain spotted fever was not east of the Mississippi River for years. I saw my first case of that out west in Missouri.

They had no nurses in what was called a nursing home. My training was so different because without nurses, I had the experience of family practice up close. The place was an old hotel that they had equipped with beds and they assigned students to every patient in that old hotel for about six months. The student had to bathe the patient, treat the patient, and nurse the patient. An orderly carried the bedpans if you weren't there. There was only a nurse to keep records and to tell you where to go. That's all the nursing there was there. There was no treatment for cancer then other than deep radiation and there was no deep radiation closer than St. Louis; even there, the radiation was so poor that it didn't justify going 200 miles for the treatment. Deep radiation would literally eat the faces, breasts, and other body parts of patients. The medical student would have to go in and wash all of those patients. You'd take bulbs with glass ends, squirt water and spray affected areas on the patients, and sometimes you even had to use the pressure of a water faucet to clean the dead tissue out. The place was horrible in smell and we had to clean it. And there was nothing that would clear the odor. They kept the nursing home close to 100 degrees all of the time. There was no air conditioning, and Missouri gets so hot and humid. What I disliked about it was getting up and having to put on wet clothes.

That's the kind of training I got that today's medical students cannot even imagine. The last year I worked in that place and irrigated those old cancers, I had a female patient, Cleo Bess, who was only 36 or 38 years old. She had multiple sclerosis and could hardly move her body and her legs. Her limbs had no feeling and the bones became just like chalk. On a Thanksgiving Day that I wasn't there, an orderly [they had orderlies to help you] pulled one of her legs or turned it and broke it in three places. It was just broken to pieces. When you picked her foot up, you could double it just like folding it up to her body. She didn't even say ouch or anything. She didn't even feel anything. Her husband had divorced her and she had two or three children. She died a year or two after I left.

When I first met her, she was full of bed sores. I had her for six months and I had all her sores cured. Dr. McClure, a neurologist, took care of her. He said, "You can cure bedsores! I gave Roland Sharp a patient who was covered with bedsores." I just put wooden swabs to the bottom of the sores and wiped them out with Merthiolate. In five or six months she was clear. She wrote me a letter after I left to thank me.

I really tried to help those people. I'm not saying that because I was a smart student. Every kid that worked there tried to do that, but today people set up hospice to take care of these types of terminal patients. They do all of the palliative treatments that help ease the patient's pain and give you some control over the end of life. It's hard to imagine that we've come that far in just sixty years. But there the patients sat and suffered. All that we could do was give them something for their pain and try to keep them as clean as we could. There were about eight or ten multiple sclerosis patients. That's a disease of the brain and spinal cord. It can be controlled a little now, but not cured. When they got down in bed, they couldn't move, and their voices would fail. They'd get real trembly and shaky. They were totally dependent. They couldn't do anything. You fed them. You cleaned them. All they had was the clothes that you put on them and the sheets and things like that. I'll always remember that.

One patient with cancer had lost most of his face. Once or twice a day, you would use a syringe and saline water and wash it into a pan and bandage him, but in two or three hours, he would need it again. The attitude of the students was better then. They would always say yes if you offered them another patient to see.

I graduated in 1943. The program in medicine was accelerated at that time due to the war and my graduation was at an odd time of the year, December 10, 1943. I continued my teaching and interning at the institution until November of 1944, and then I moved on.

Internship in Ohio

When I went to medical school, I was a professor as well as a student. I went over and over these things, class after class after class, for ten semesters, which was far more valuable to me than my internship. When I got into the internship, I had already been into more and been through more than the other students who had come for the same thing. My training when I came out of medical school was probably equivalent to three years of residency, because I had completed four years of school and ten semesters of teaching. I learned more teaching than I learned as a student because you have to know what you're teaching pretty thoroughly. All of the kids I was teaching those ten semesters had anywhere from three years [of undergraduate studies] to a master's degree.

Although teaching taught me a lot, my teaching didn't quite give me enough training in obstetrics and surgery. So I applied to Green Cross Hospital in Akron, Ohio to do two rotations. I spent the next three months up there in rotations in surgery and obstetrics. I had had those rotations at Kirksville, but I missed a lot of it because babies would be born while I was in my teaching period or my laboratory periods, or there would be emergency surgery—surgery that I felt I should see—while I was in lecture room or in laboratory. So I got rotations in those areas in Akron. As a result I think when I went into practice I was better trained than the average doctor because I had delivered a lot more babies and I had scrubbed in on a lot more surgeries.

Your rotations were usually a month long. When I was in Akron, do you know what I got? - Twenty five dollars a month for my food, my uniforms, laundry, and one half-day off every three weeks. There were three interns at that hospital because they couldn't get any more interns. Each intern got a half-day off. One would get it off one week; another would get it off the next week. So we had a half-day every three weeks to spend that twenty five dollars. You couldn't even buy a meal because of the war. Nothing was open. I guess I was really lucky in the experience that I gained beyond what average doctors got.

I assisted in surgery six mornings a week from seven until one or two o'clock in the afternoon. You'd just finish one surgery, take off your gown, and put on another one for another surgery because there was a scarcity of surgeons. There were only two surgeons in that whole hospital. And there were several obstetricians, older ones, and they had ten obstetrical beds. All of those were licensed. They were licensed for so many beds—so many medical beds, so many obstetrical beds—and you could not put medical and surgical patients in obstetrical beds for fear of cross-contamination. Ohio had a very strict law that no medical patients were permitted in obstetrical beds and no surgical patients in obstetrical beds, for fear of the woman being cross-contaminated with disease or infection.

During the three months I was there, all ten obstetrical beds were filled. You would have a patient in the waiting room in labor waiting for a bed. Akron was that crowded with people. It was really an overcrowded city because all of the rubber plants were working day and night to supply tires for the military. So you had accidents day and night. You constantly had families in there that were giving birth. They were young people, families. So I think I had better than average training because of the three intense months there.

See, I was supposed to have a six-week rotation in surgery and a six-week rotation in obstetrics, but when I was on the rotation in obstetrics, I was on call. You didn't just sit and wait for a baby to come in. I had to go back to surgery and scrub in unless there was an obstetrical call. Then I would often just go back and forth constantly. So I really got three months of training in obstetrics and three months of training in surgery. Every morning, I was in surgery from seven in the morning until two in the afternoon. Obstetrics was all night long, all day and all night. For some reason, most of the babies came at night. I worked all morning and night, and lived right in the hospital. I lived in the basement of the hospital. Your interns lived there. You had your food and a uniform and a bed. So in my three months there I didn't leave very many times, only a half day every three weeks or so. There was nothing to go to anyway. There was a war on.

When you weren't busy in your internship rotation, they used the interns to make the surgical packages for surgery that usually the surgical nurse does. You put everything in a package, pinned it, and folded it up for them to use. I laugh and joke now that most of the interns today can't open the package in surgery. We had to put it together. You make a certain package for a gall bladder surgery, a different kind of package for an appendectomy, a different kind of big package for a hysterectomy, and a different package for a delivery. They all go in a big autoclave and are sterilized. The nurse puts them on the table and the intern opens them. I hadn't had that training.

Most of us couldn't open the package even though we had put it together. But I never regretted it. I always thought that was a plus for us and I never regretted any of the extra times that I had to work.

I remember working with one obstetrician, Dr. Bond, in Akron. He was a medical graduate from Thomas Jefferson University in Philadelphia. Like a lot of people, he had his oddities. He wore a vest all of the time. His vest pocket was always full of candy corn. He'd walk around and tell you about this patient. He'd take one and he'd hand you one, almost subconsciously. He'd feed you corn when you went with him following his rounds.

During one of my first experiences with him, we delivered a set of twins, a boy and a girl. Afterwards, he delivered the afterbirth. When you deliver the afterbirth, a good doctor always takes it up with a sponge and wipes it completely clean and clear. If there are any little pieces broken off of the afterbirth, that piece is going to be in the mother's uterus and she's going to hemorrhage. So you wipe that off carefully and make sure that every bit of it is there so you don't have trouble. Dr. Bond wiped this one off, threw it over in the pan, and said, "Well, we've got identical twins."

Interns are not supposed to say a word. However, I had been a teacher of embryology, developmental anatomy—that's the baby before it's born. I said, "No, we don't, Doc." He said, "What the hell do you know about it?" I said, "One's a girl and one's a boy." He said, "Oh." After that I guess he must have decided I knew something about it. I delivered twenty six babies after that by myself without his help. When he talked to me a little about it, he didn't say he was going to let me deliver babies.

With forty percent of the patients in obstetrics who came in that hospital, what the intern was supposed to do was take the history and say "Who's your doctor?" Whenever they tell you the doctor, you go right to the telephone and say, "We have your obstetrical patient." He always told me, "Take her in the delivery room. I'll be right there in a few minutes." I'd take her in the labor room. She'd be in labor a few minutes. I'd call him. "I'll be there in just a few minutes now." And he always arranged to get there fifteen or twenty minutes after the baby was born! He let me deliver all the babies. I know he was letting me do that. Once in a while he'd come in maybe when I was cutting the cord. I was saving him a lot of time, and at least when I made that comment, "No, they're not. One's a boy and one's a girl," I hit it off well with him.

He was a good friend the whole time I was there. After the hospital moved and rebuilt in Cuyahoga Falls, I lost touch with him. I'm sure that he's passed on because he was an older man at that time. But the incident of the identical and fraternal twins and the candy corn put him down as one of my most unforgettable characters. I guess that's what you would call him.

So as a result, I really got a lot of good experience up there. Dr. C.L. Vallinger was chief of surgery. Time and again he would say, "You just sign up for another year here." I didn't want to be a surgeon and I always came back with, "Oh, Dr. Vallinger, I'm afraid of blood. Blood scares me." He'd just look up at me and grin.

Medical Training Today

Practice today isn't like it was when I went to medical school. I'm not throwing off or looking down on any doctor, but I think doctors were taught more when I was a student. When I started in medical school in Morgantown, they said, "You are to be in that seat every day".

There was no such thing as an excused absence in medical school. If you're ill and can't be there, you see me and we will make up what you missed. Most medical schools require attendance, but there are medical schools today where they go home, they use the computer, TV, or something like that. They miss a lot. You can't tell me they don't miss a lot. I know they learn a lot more about other things though.

I think the important things you learn when you're a resident, an intern, or a student are things that you actually see and that are "hands on." You hear the doctor tell of his experience with this kind of a patient and you can see reel after reel of anatomy, but it's the anatomy that you're dissecting while he's describing it to you that you remember.

In your internship you were required to be there twenty four hours a day or to be available twenty four hours a day, with what I told you, twenty-five or thirty dollars [of pay per month]. When I was at the hospital at Kirksville, I didn't get anything but my uniform. That was a teaching hospital. It was a privilege to be there. I didn't even think of that. I was a paid faculty member, so I figured I was getting a good deal. Do you know what they pay interns now? $25,000 a year. They have hours. I'm not resentful. I'm just glad I got my good education and I really think I got a good education because I could compete with any of the doctors who I've practiced around. I didn't consider myself superior. I considered that in every field I felt equal or better than they were.

Dr. Richard Meiling, the vice provost of the College of Medicine at Ohio State, told me that he thought that residencies were the biggest joke in medicine. He was certified in gynecological surgery and pathology and was a man sixty-five to seventy years old when I met him. He came as an advisor when we started the medical school in Lewisburg and we had a three-day visit. We had an opportunity to just talk to each other about our practice and our training. His statement was, "Residencies are a farce. A three-year residency doesn't guarantee you that a surgeon could amputate your tongue. I have trained surgeons in residency that I wouldn't turn loose on anybody, but they have completed their residency and are eligible to take the certification board. I have had other residents who in six months could do any kind of complicated surgery that we had to offer. There is that much difference. Just because a doctor is certified in his field doesn't indicate in any way his competency." Now that was a top educator. As Dr. Meiling said, there's incompetence at the top medical schools in the country and there are people who border on genius in some of the little outskirts.

Doctors as Thinkers

It sounds like I might be giving doctors a hard time, but I'm not. I'm going to make a statement that I make to a lot of patients. The worst place to have a heart attack is in a doctor's office, unless it's a cardiologist, or a general practitioner, or unless there's someone in there who knows something about CPR. A lot of specialists wouldn't even have a blood pressure apparatus or a stethoscope. They say, "I just look at eyes or look at skin."

You very much have to be a better thinker to be a family doctor than to be a specialist and you have to keep up on all these subjects because you don't know, for example, what skin conditions will come in. You don't know what type of infections you will see. You've got to have a full catalogue of knowledge and tools in the back of your mind. You must know when someone comes in and complains of a pain how many surgical possibilities there are. You can rule them out right in your office, or with a little lab work, or with the facilities we have right here in the local hospital - ultrasound, blood tests, etcetera. It just takes an extra two days or something like that. You can have endoscopy, gastroscopy, colonoscopy. When you do those things, you don't need all of these other complicated things like MRIs if you're a good problem solver.

A lot more attention should be paid to the doctor's ability to solve problems. I came to the conclusion that the mediocre student was as good a thinker or person for general medicine as the top students I had in the class. Some of the top students I had could answer any question you asked them, but they couldn't solve any problem.

Now, an examination was designed about twenty five years ago called FLEX; the Federation Licensing Examination. The Federation of State Medical Boards in the United States and

Canada designed that board exam. It was in three parts. At the end of two years they gave students the first part. The first part was totally technically academic. On this part, the top students showed a marked advantage above the average students. There was a wide space between the top and the bottom. At the end of four years, they gave them the second part. The second part was academic and diagnostic. When they got to the second part, student scores were closer together. At the end of a rotating internship they gave them the third part. The third part was problem solving. There was so little difference in these scores that they couldn't distinguish between the lowest student in the class and the highest. I served on the Licensing Board in West Virginia for twenty one years, and I still receive their monthly bulletin, so I'm not talking through my hat here. They've since phased FLEX out

Of those who were top students in my class, I can't think of more than one or two that I would ever go to as a doctor. There were students with mediocre grades, because I came in during the war and they took C+ students at that time. That was the only time in the last ninety years that there weren't enough applicants to fill the medical schools. So you took who you could get.

Two of the best students I ever taught never had any premed. During the war they admitted you to medical school as long as you had a degree. They gave them short courses in chemistry and the other premed subjects in a quick year. They could use a microscope as well as biology and chemistry majors, and their grades were tops. One was a Jewish man from New York and one was a woman on the faculty at the University of Illinois. She was middle-aged. She and her husband wanted to do something for the war, but they were too old to be drafted, so they came to medical school. She practiced for thirty years and was really a fine physician.

You can't teach people to be thinkers in medical school. They have to learn that before. I think people are born with critical thinking skills as opposed to memorizing skills. In medical school and as a doctor, you have to do more than memorize material. You've got to piece it together. Critical thinking skills ought to be taken into consideration a lot more in the selection of medical school students.

I've told students, "If I were ever called on to testify against you, I won't fault anyone for judgment, but I would if you attempted to do something you're not trained to do. After all, you're dealing with human lives."

A lot more attention should be paid to the doctor's actual past. In other words I feel that they should be recommended by half or three-fourths of their college professors instead of being recommended by three or four prominent people in the community or by the premed advisor. The premed advisor is going to give the best recommendation to the student he likes the best. That's just being human I think. I think that a chemistry professor, a biology professor, and a physics professor could tell you about the student. Probably the guy in physics could tell you the most.

Doctoring in the Coal Fields

1945–1962

"In my career, I delivered two thousand or more babies. Most all were delivered at home."
—Roland Sharp

I finished medical school too late to be drafted. By the time the school released me, the war was almost over. You see, the school couldn't release me earlier because I was teaching. The War Department had written me when I tried to enlist and told me, "Your service is more important where you are. When we want you we'll call you." I finished school in December 1943, and by the time I completed my internship, it was the end of 1944. The war ended in 1945. When I asked the draft board or applied for a commission, they said, "We've got all the doctors we need. There's not nearly enough at home."

That's how I went to the coalfields. Jennings Randolph was the congressman from the Second District [of West Virginia] then. I wrote to him for his assistance in getting me a commission in the medical corps of the army or navy. He told me, "I think I could get one, but it would be better for you to go home. West Virginia is really in dire need. If I were you, I would go to Wyoming [County] or Putnam County. They don't have enough doctors to even deliver the babies." The Surgeon General had told him that even if I were commissioned, I would have to go into civilian practice anyway.

There wasn't Medicare then, and a good many doctors were looking for paid jobs after the war instead of going out into private practice. I would always prefer private practice. I only went into industrial medicine for one reason, because of the scarcity. The United Mine Workers [UMW] and the other unions were advertising in medical magazines, and there was one in my school's magazine for thirty five doctors in District 29 of the UMW, which covers from Beckley south in West Virginia. The UMW had only just recently negotiated the right to hire the union's own doctor.

Only a couple of us responded then. The student body in medical schools had dropped during the war. Instead of applying to medical school, students were enlisting to be in service because it was the patriotic thing everybody thought to do, including myself. After the war the student body in medical schools began to pick up and more and more doctors came to West Virginia until there were fifteen or twenty coal company doctors, quite a few from the school that I attended. It took me a long time to find out how the mine workers knew about the school, but about ten years later I learned that George Titler, who was president of UMW's District 29 in Beckley, was born and raised in Missouri. He knew all about osteopathic physicians. He had put the ad in the journal at the school in Kirksville.

I moved back to West Virginia, to Mullens, in late 1944 and started as a coal company doctor for the workers of the West Gulf Coal Company in April 1945. I was told I was the first doctor in the country to sign a contract with the UMW directly, as opposed to through the coal company.

Of course I had come directly from Akron, Ohio, where I had just finished my rotations in obstetrics and surgery. Those were probably the most exciting twelve weeks of my life. There was hardly time to get a shower and grab a new uniform!

Coal Company Doctor

When I started practicing medicine it was quite different from today, and the kind of practice I had then was different from the kind of practice I have today [interview held in the year 2000].

Mullens, West Virginia, mid twentieth century. Photo courtesy of the Eastern Regional Coal Archives, Craft Memorial Library, Bluefield, West Virginia.

Being a coal company doctor, I was employed first by the coal company and then by the UMW, and that meant that you had patients from the very day that you opened the office[4]. We opened my private practice office November 22, 1944, in Mullens, and the first day I opened my coal company office, April 11, 1945, I must have had fifteen or twenty patients.

In Mullens there was no waiting for patients. During the first seven days down there, I delivered eight babies. So you know, to be a new doctor coming in the community and have that much business, they must have been in dire need. When you became a company doctor, they announced you. It was just like opening the door when they're having a big sale at J.C. Penney's or something. When you went to the office to open the door, there'd be people lined up out there. You'd open the door, walk in, and the waiting room quickly filled up. When you are in private practice, there'll be two or three or something like that at a time and they'll call and tell you they're coming. That is much more desirable.

In the coal towns they never called to tell you or anything. They'd walk in bleeding, with the room full of patients. On the other hand, the coal company patients in general were nice people—good, kind, understanding people. I had great friends there.

Medicine was rather different from what it is today because you were expected to make house calls and I made eight or ten every day. I didn't have penicillin at the time I started—the armed services were using it all for the war effort. The only thing you had to fight infection with was sulfa drugs. However, penicillin became common within the next three years.

On an average day, I would go to the coal company office at eight in the morning and stay until ten. Then I would make house calls from ten until noon in the town of Maben, five miles

---

[4] A certain amount was deducted from each man's payday for medical services, which covered all visits to the company doctor. The monthly charge when Dr. Sharp started was three dollars a month.

north of Mullens, which was a W.M. Ritter Lumber Company town before it became a West Gulf Coal Company town. You saw patients at home with very little wrong with them most of the time. Occasionally you would see a sick one, but most of the time they just called you because it was more convenient to have you come to the house than it was for them to go to the office. Since you were their company doctor and they were paying you by the month for this service, they wanted you at the house. That's like Medicare. A few people will constantly abuse the program. But eighty percent of the people wouldn't see me even once a year.

Just a few had the idea, "Well, I pay the doctor. I ought to see him anytime I want!" But that was only a minor group, maybe twenty patients who stopped in all the time. But if it's ten percent of your patients who do that, it'll wear you out. I had two families there I must have seen 500 times in seventeen years.

In Maben you saw a hundred patients a day. It was prepaid and gave me a good idea of what socialized medicine would be like. Three-quarters of the families that came in to see you didn't have anything wrong with them. They just came in because they were paying the doctor. They passed the office and just stopped in.

They'd say, "We'd like a few headache tablets."

So you'd say, "Well, do you have a headache? Let me look at you."

"Oh no, I don't have a headache. I had one yesterday. I just need some headache tablets."

Some patient would come in, "I've had a dizzy spell. I want to know what caused it."

"Well, tell me how you feel."

"Oh, that was last week. I don't remember how it was, but anyway I was dizzy for about fifteen minutes. I just thought you could give me something to keep me from having it again." I remember one family in particular. I don't remember when they didn't have two or three members of the family in every day—

for five straight years! Not only that, I made house calls four or five times a week just to look at their baby's ears. "Is it crying?"

"No, it's pulling its ear. I thought it might have an earache. We put in a call for you because we thought we might save you a trip some other time."

When we got to Mullens, Opal immediately went to work at my office. And she got better and better in the office and could do anything. Basically, she taught our office help all the little things in the office; how to answer the telephone, what to tell a patient when they were calling about this and that. Us doctors there didn't do that. She did that, and she worked in the office twenty-five years or more, until she had trained everybody in my office, even the registered nurses that worked. She helped them a lot, and, believe it or not, none of them resented it, because she was just such a smart woman.

Time and again, I thought she should have been a doctor. Dr. Jim Price knew us well in Marlinton. Dr. Jim, every time we went in there while I was in medical school, said "She should go to school. Let her go after you." She was happy with what she was doing. She never did say, "I'd like to go." She never even mentioned that.

In Mullens I had a car to get to patients' homes. I went into practice before the war ended and you couldn't get a car, so I had the same old car for ten years. Then I got a Jeep, a Jeep station wagon, and I used up three of those going out on the mountains. The dirt roads were full of rocks people had thrown in the road to get in and out of the mud or snow. My good patients who lived along there would come out and drag me out every time I got stuck. But every time they dragged me, they dragged some more of the bottom of the car out as well.

I remember one particular incident. I went on one mountain with the old car to deliver a baby and got twenty-five or thirty dollars and it cost fifty or sixty dollars to put the underside of the car back on. The whole exhaust system was torn off. It was way back on those mountains, but I didn't complain about it. I was glad to do it. People were good then and really respected the doctor. I mean they appreciated me. I don't know how many hams I carried home, dozens of eggs, beef. They loaded you up with everything like that. That was in addition to the three dollars a month they paid you.

When I started, there were 365 to 370 company employees. Most of them were married, so you could figure out the families of 365 men or so. Maybe twenty or thirty would be single, but the rest would be married men with families. When I left, there were only about a fraction of the number and they were mining more coal. Things had changed. When I first went there, they had this large number of men because they were digging coal manually with a pick and shoveling it into cars. When I left, they were doing all of it mechanically with what were called continuous miners, which had rotating wheels with big iron claws up front to grind up coal just like an auger. They go along a seam of coal and fill little two wheel carts behind. All they needed was for someone to disconnect that little cart and hook another one to the machine. All they had to do was dump that one load into a coal car. Very little of it was loaded by hand.

Now they'll mine as much coal as they used to in those days and they'll continue to, but it doesn't take many people to do it. You just take ten or fifteen men, and they have to be pretty well educated. They have to be able to operate computers and to be able to read the directions for maintaining that complex machinery. Before, fifty percent of those miners could not sign their name. Those miners had come up from the Carolinas, the mountains of Virginia, and Kentucky, and the company paid cash. They put the cash in the envelope, and before they handed you your envelope, you wrote your signature, and the miners had to mark for their pay. The payroll clerk showed me his ledger. One day he was telling me about it, but it was hard for me to believe that so many couldn't write. So he just turned the sheet around like that and said, "Look at all the Xs on those two sheets." He had opened the pay register and there were the marks the miners had made as their signatures. These were

Typical miners' housing in the coal camps of southern West Virginia in the 1940s. Photo courtesy of National Archives Still Pictures, College Park, Maryland.

kind, considerate people. They just hadn't received an education.

Delivering Babies Up in the Mountains

The deliveries were quite different from those that we have today. At that time having a baby at home was no big deal. That was the rule instead of the exception. However, it was quite an experience when I started. In medical school and in my obstetrics internship, I had seen a lot of deliveries and helped with a whole lot of deliveries, but all of the deliveries that are done in medical school are done in the hospital. As a matter of fact, when I went in practice, I had seen only one home delivery.

I went out to people's homes. I delivered 1,200 to 1,500 babies in their homes for twenty-five dollars each. You were paid through the coal company. Each worker paid three dollars a month for your service and twenty-five dollars extra for delivering a baby. My last five years there, they raised the assessment to five dollars per employee and fifty dollars for a delivery. Since the camps no longer needed so many workers, they didn't want to lose my services.

You went all over the mountains and all through the coal camps and your day was about eighteen hours. There was so much obstetrics. You had a bad week if you didn't have five or six babies that week. Some weeks you would deliver eight or ten.

I remember, I think it was 1949, when someone from the Beckley paper came in and said there were prizes for the first baby born on New Year's Day.

The reporter said, "We're looking for the baby that was born first."

"I'll have to get the book out here and look."

"You mean you had more than one?"

And when I sat down with this man, I think it was Ben Murphy, I had delivered twelve babies in seven days, the first seven days in January of 1949. He went back and wrote an article about that. But mine wasn't the first. I think the first one was maybe midday, but in the twenty four hours following midnight, I delivered two or three babies. He wrote a story that the doctor in Mullens had delivered twelve babies in the first week of the month. He wrote down where each one was born. This one was Black Eagle, this one was Maben, this was Barker's Ridge, and this one was Allen Junction, etcetera. Then he calculated the mileage from Mullens out to this place, and Mullens to that one, and to all those deliveries. He figured that I had driven 200 to 300 miles, had regular office hours, and delivered all of those babies. I have that thing somewhere in my files. I think it was the *Raleigh Register*.

One time, the first year, I climbed across Bowers Mountain to deliver a baby—where Twin Falls State Park is now. You couldn't get in with a car in the wintertime. So you went on a road until you had to stop. Then you had to walk up a high mountain. The father came over the ridge and got me, and he carried one medical bag, and I carried the other. It took us about an hour to walk across and down the other side, and I was there for five hours.

The man's name was Jim Bowers. His ancestors were the original people in Wyoming County—schoolteachers from North Carolina who came to that wild and uninhabited country. All nine children of the Bowers family became teachers.

I remember it well. When we got through, he said, "Now Doctor, I'm going to pay you for this and I'm going to give you a ham of meat and a part of a quarter of a beef. I just killed a beef and I keep hogs back here." And he gave me a fifty dollar bill.

I said, "Mr. Bowers, I really appreciate it. That's nice of you to do it, but there's no way I could carry all of that out of here."

He said, "Doc, don't worry. I got people to carry that over." He had already recruited neighbors to take fifty pounds of beef and a couple hams across that mountain to my car at the Phillips place.

In my career, I delivered about two thousand or more babies. Most all were delivered at home.

Soapsuds

We company doctors depended on one another. If one was gone...well, there were deliveries every day, practically. If one was gone or had to be away for a couple of hours, he would usually call the other doctor and say, "I'm telling these people to call you." That evening, someone called me from the Baileysville-Davy Road in McDowell County. They said, "This was Dr. Mervin Meck's patient and he said you would take care of it."

They said it was very, very primitive living quarters, but I want to impress upon you what wonderful people lived in such areas. Even though those people lived in primitive quarters, they had hearts of gold. I drove into this very rustic place. I went in and checked the lady and I saw that she wasn't bathed very well. Whenever you went to deliver babies, there were three or four women around. That is kosher in rural areas. And they always had three or four gallons of hot water on the coal cooking stove.

I asked one of those ladies, "Will you please give her a good bath and please wash the hair real well?"

That was useless. I waited for a half hour and I went to the door and knocked.

"Are you through?" About twenty minutes later, they came in and got another ten-quart bucket of water and brought that back. I had rubber gloves on. Back then, they didn't have the plastic type and if you wore rubber gloves for a couple of hours, your hands were just burnt. I went about three times to the door and inquired over a period of I'd say an hour. And the door rubbed on the floor. You couldn't open it and go in. So I just took my foot and pushed. I had the rubber gloves on and didn't want to get my hands dirty.

When I looked in there I almost fainted. Behind the bed there was lather halfway up the wall and it was all over the door. One woman looked at me so pitifully and said, "Doctor, we can't get her hair washed. We turn her over here and put her head down in the tub to rinse. And she has a pain, and she throws her head back, and she slops it all over, and that's where all the lather came from. We're doing the best we can."

I said, "Please don't worry about it."

They hadn't touched that woman's body at all. So I just sponged her off. I should have told them to wash the pubic hair! That was an uneventful delivery, but it was one that flabbergasted me. I never saw so many soapsuds and lather in one bedroom in my life.

That Mills Baby

Another time I went down in the deep holler on Barker's Ridge to deliver a young lady, her first baby. It was so steep going down. It must have been 500 feet to the road. They had dug out places to walk like steps. This girl was living with her grandmother. Well, I went clear down into that hollow. You couldn't get anything but a horse in there if you had problems. There was no way to get a vehicle in there. She would have had to be carried out by people.

I went up there on a Wednesday afternoon. The sun was shining. Grandma Mills was the lady of the house. She lived in a log house with three rooms. You go in this one, through the next door, then out the last one, three rooms. The first room was the kitchen. The second room was where this girl was in labor. The third one was where the grandmother's invalid brother, who was about seventy or eighty years old, was in bed. I checked the girl in the afternoon. Wednesday afternoon was the only time I had a lull. Often, employees could take extra time off on a Wednesday. So I was glad to be out on that mountain. I said, "It's going to be several hours for this, but it's too far to go back to Mullens." It was about eight or ten miles out of Mullens. I said, "It's so far back, I'm just going to stay here."

So I asked Mrs. Mills, "Do you have plenty of light? It may be after dark when this baby comes."

She said, "Yes." So I sat down there in the sunshine and talked to a young boy. He was about nineteen or something like that, the father. We talked and looked out over the mountains. There was nothing to see but mountains. I talked to Mrs. Mills. We had supper and the girl still wasn't ready to deliver.

I said, "It's going to be later than I thought. So I want to be sure about the light." They had a cook stove and the woman was lighting the house by taking the lid off the stove while it was burning. It would light the room about like a candle.

She said, "We'll light the lamp later." She had two carbide lamps, but they had only a small amount in them.

Time went on, and it was getting closer to midnight, so I went to Mrs. Mills, and I said, "She is pretty well dilated, and I think we're going to need the light, so fix it up in the room. All my things are boiled and ready."

About ten minutes later, Mrs. Mills came in wringing her hands like that and said, "Doctor, the carbide can's empty!" I nearly fell over. Those carbide lamps weren't going to last.

Carbide light is all they had. I had no light. The lamp just burned around thirty minutes. The carbide went out, and that's all the light we had. At one o'clock the baby was ready to deliver. She started up the fire in the cook stove and took a couple of lids off of it, and a little light would flicker in there, but it didn't reach my patient. And so I delivered that baby with forceps in the dark! And the mother got along well, but you couldn't tell whether she was bleeding or hemorrhaging after it. All I could do was rub that rubber glove on the bed and see whether the odor was that of blood or the amniotic fluid that's around the baby. I stayed until daylight and sat with the girl to make sure she was safe. I cut the cord in the dark, cleaned up the baby, and sat there in the dark until daylight. I was too scared to leave.

I had such a headache that I could hardly walk. The boy made a couple of trips to help me carry everything back to the car. It took two or three bags—one was a special OB bag—to carry everything to the top there. My head ached until I could hardly manage myself on those dirt steps, all from the stress of that night.

When I got home, I said to my wife, "I'm getting out of this country. I'm never going to deliver another baby."

Opal just looked at me and I said, "With the headache I had." I told her what I had done—that I had delivered the baby in the dark.

She said, "I think you're probably supposed to be here or God wouldn't have let you do that. You couldn't have gotten through last night alone. Don't talk silly. Just go back to work."

I think that was one of the most touching experiences between a patient and me, and between Opal and me. When she said, "You better be glad you just have a headache. Don't you know that God had something to do with that or you wouldn't have had a nice big healthy eight-pound baby?"

And the woman really didn't hemorrhage to amount to anything. But I couldn't tell when the afterbirth was expelling or anything. I believe I am the only person I have ever met who delivered a baby with forceps in solid darkness.

I told that story to three obstetricians from Yale at the AMA [American Medical Association] Congress on Medical Education in Chicago. They were sitting with me in a meeting, asked me what I did, and I told them I was a coal company doctor. Of course, they wanted to know what you did in a coal camp. I told them the story of delivering that baby and they invited me to dinner with the Yale OB faculty. They wanted me to tell the story and they paid for my dinner at the Palmer House in Chicago. I don't think they believed half of it.

I told this story once at the Union League in Philadelphia. Dr. Schwartz from Des Moines laid a dollar bill beside my plate.

"What's that for?" I asked.

"It's for the damned biggest liar I ever listened to!" And he wouldn't take the dollar back.

That was just one of many challenging birthing experiences, but it was one that I will never forget. I think God has to be with you and I'll always remember that old lady coming in, wringing her hands and saying, "Doctor, the carbide can is empty!" And I'll tell you - my heart fell clear down to the seat of my pants. That baby was coming right then. I could feel the top of its head, but it wasn't going to come by itself. There was nothing to do but use forceps, and I did.

After that, I told some of my colleagues that I could deliver a baby with forceps anywhere. I've already learned to do that totally by feel, not by sight and what you learn in the book is a lot of stuff you can't put in practice. I think that if I had told my professors that story, they would have said, "You're totally crazy. Totally crazy!"

Accidents at the Mines

When an accident happened at the mine, they called me. Sometimes you would go in the mine and sometimes they would already have the person out by the time you got there. There's never anything you can do. The only thing that a company doctor can do in case of an accident is remove fingers or toes. They mash their fingers and toes frequently. I expect I would have had a wastebasket full of toes.

Whenever I saw someone who said he was going to be a brakeman, I would always warn him, "I'll see you in six months."

He'd usually say, "What for?"

I'd say, "For one of your fingers. You won't keep your fingers out. You have to pull a pin up to disconnect the car."

There were twelve fatal accidents while I was at one of the mines. In the other mine, there was just one accident. The mine that had one accident used conveyors. You put coal on the conveyor, which was like an escalator. That would bring the coal out. Sometimes those would reach three or four mines. But even the conveyor wasn't without danger. There were three or four men who lost arms and legs that slipped into the conveyor.

At the other mine, I can think of only two or three accidents that didn't involve violations of safety regulations. The first death was a foreman, a shop foreman from Beckley, who came in one very cold—subzero—morning. He thought the fire was out in the stove, and he took out the gasoline can and poured it in the stove.

You cannot believe it. That five-gallon can exploded until it looked like you had run over it with a tractor-trailer. I never would have dreamed that gas had that power, but I later found out that gas explodes. It does not burn. Oil and kerosene burn and do not explode. Anyway, this man had a huge heavy mackinaw and two or three coats underneath. He didn't burn his shoulders, but from his waist down he had just cooked himself. He lived three weeks, but he was the most resigned of any man I ever saw. He told me on the way to the hospital, "If I had a man working for me who did a trick like that, I would fire him on the spot."

He was one of the few I went to the hospital with—Beckley was twenty five miles away—because I thought there would be a lot of pain. I wanted to be there to treat that. There was too much infection and he had burned his tendons until his legs were just pulled up. I know he was in great pain, but he never complained. He turned to me and said, "I have had three chances. God gave me three chances. I was called to the ministry when I was a certain age and I backed out. I was called a second time and I backed down. In the last year I was called again and I didn't listen. I got just what I deserved."

That's unusual to hear someone say something like that. He was the calmest I've ever seen anyone facing death. That story still touches me. I went to see him several times over those weeks. The last time, maybe four days before he died, he was fully rational.

Some of the tragic ones - one man was cut in two when the mine motor wheels ran over him. Brakemen were usually the ones who lost their hands, arms, and legs. This one mine that had a lot of accidents was a mine with a track and a motor - a machine to pull coal cars. The capacity of each car was twenty tons and sometimes the motor would pull fifteen or twenty of

Miners in southern West Virginia around 1950. Photo courtesy of the Eastern Regional Coal Archives, Craft Memorial Library, Bluefield, West Virginia.

those cars. And for people who can't understand; inside a mine is just like this; your seam of coal doesn't run straight back. It will go up. It will go down. And it is anywhere from thirty inches to four feet in height. There is a hard and fast rule or safety regulation - no brakeman gets off the motor from the back. He gets off the side. Those who got off the back were often killed when the motor ran over them. This brakeman was practically severed. The only thing that kept the motor from totally severing him in half was his spine.

Another disturbing violation involved a man who came in to be examined for employment. He had completed two years of college work. A man who had two years college work back in those days had no business in the mine. Back then they were digging coal with a pick and loading it with a shovel.

"Well, I don't know anything I could make more money at. I'm going to go at it for a while, and then I'll probably go back to college." He was what they call a supply man. He arrived at eleven o'clock in the evening and loaded his motor with supplies to be delivered to the site where the miners were working.

Then he asked the dispatcher, "Is it clear? Are there any more motors in there?"

The dispatcher said, "It's all clear." That was a serious mistake.

He wasn't inside a mile when a big twenty-ton motor with fifteen or twenty cars was coming out, and it was running out of control. It was running loose. I mean if you don't have good brakemen, the coal cars will push the motor right on. They hit him so hard that it drove him right up into the ceiling of the mine, crushing him. That was one of the things I really regretted.

The last fatality there did not involve a violation of anything. It was almost an act of God. When you dig coal you put a board up and set a prop on each side—that's called timbering— to hold up the mine ceiling then you dig a little more. You don't go under that. You just dig out as far as you safely can and then you decide what to do next. This man was an old gentleman and a real good friend. He was already drawing his Social Security, but he hadn't worked in the mines long enough to earn the miners' welfare [pension]. He said he wanted to work another year until he could get that. They said he was the safest man in that mine. He set his timber up. When he got it set up, he just stuck his head up through that crossbeam to see how it looked and the whole thing fell. His head was crushed. That was a real tragedy. By the way, if you're at the Twin Falls State Park, his farm was a part of that. That's all now part of that beautiful park. At least he had that legacy.

To Go on Vacation

When you worked for the coal company, the only time you left was when you had a doctor to cover your practice. We would take our vacations in the summer. We would take four to six weeks and come up to Frost in the summer. I would get a doctor to cover. We would leave Mullens about the first of June and stay up here in Frost from June to the middle part of July. See, doctors who were interning would finish their internship in June and they were anxious to make some money to get started in practice. Covering my practice was quick money because I gave the doctors who worked for me half of everything that came in. It was no trouble to get doctors in.

I first began taking students after I went into practice when the war ended. I took students who wanted to be trained in rural medicine or industrial medicine. When I was in Mullens, I was taking students who wanted to be in industrial medicine, those who wanted to take salaried positions for companies. My son was a medical student then and he wrote to me and said, "I have a good friend who is really a fine doctor and a great intern. If you can use him this summer while you're on vacation, please do me a favor."

I took Dr. Ward and it turned out really well. He was later one of the most successful ear, nose, and throat specialists on the west coast of Florida. When Dr. Ward, who owns farms in

Pocahontas County today, finished his internship, he came to Mullens and stayed five or six weeks. He went back to his residency for the winter and then came back to Mullens the next summer for six weeks. He came back each summer to Mullens because he and his wife have told me time and time again that that was the only spending money, the only extra money, he had for his three years in residency.

Mullens was indeed a good place to train young doctors in the demanding world of medicine. Afterward I would tell his patients in Florida, "He's the only ENT specialist who's delivered babies out in the mountains!"

Paul

My son Paul graduated from Mullens High School. He went to Marlinton High School one semester, and then came to Mullens and started in Mullens High School, I believe, the second semester, and he graduated from Mullens High School in 1950.

Paul was extremely well built. He was an excellent baseball player. When he went to high school, he went out for football, the second or third year. He was a good football player. The next year he went out for football and the coach said, "We're not going to let you play." Immediately, of course, he asked "Why?" He was an excellent trumpet player. The coach said, "You're first trumpeter in the band, and the band instructor said he needed a first trumpet worse than I need a football player." And Paul never did get over abusing me some for him not being on the football team. I went to college with the coach, and I told the coach he was a really good trumpet player.

Now, back to his trumpet playing. One of Harry James' trumpeters was a student at the medical school, and he gave Paul his lessons. Well, Foozy [Charles Bragg] wasn't the best student, and I give Foozy some extra attention. And he just said to me one day, when we were talking about trumpet playing, "Foozy, I want my son to take some sort of music."

"Oh, I'll give him lessons."

So, he came out to our house for a couple of years, and Paul and Foozy got to be great friends. Paul was just in grade school, but they got to be friends. And when we were leaving Kirksville, he gave him a gold trumpet that he played with Harry James.

From Mullens High Paul went to Greenbrier Military School. [This campus later became the school of osteopathic medicine.] Greenbrier Military School had a junior college, and he got two years credit there. He was on their first team wrestling and boxing at the military school. Then he went to Concord one year, and Concord did not have organic chemistry. So, he transferred to the University of Virginia for organic chemistry. He did very well, and when we were talking with the admissions officer, he asked him, "Would you go - Would you be interested in staying here for medical school?" The University of Virginia, at that time, just required two years of pre-med, and Paul didn't give him an answer at that time. He just said he would think about it.

Oh, he probably was thinking about going to osteopathic school when we left Kirksville because he loved the place, and he loved the school, and also Northeast Missouri State is located there. And, he thought about that as a college to go to where he would be able to live in a place that he liked, and a lot of students that he liked. I think that was one of the things that drew him back there. And, when we went back to the UVA admission office, this same officer, when he said, "Well, what's your decision? What do you think about coming to school here?" I can remember Paul twisting it around a little and saying, "Oh, I think…" – He talked with a drawl or something, maybe he took it after me or something – "I think I'll go to the [Kirksville] school. My dad went there." That was just the way it ended.

Paul liked farming very much, and if I had been able to have bought my farm here at Frost before he went to medical school, I don't believe I could have convinced him that he should go on to medical school. This place was for sale. He looked this place all over. He had walked all over it with my father and he and my father were just like this. My dad walked the fences on this place with Paul, and we made them an offer, which they did not accept at that time. [Dr, Sharp bought the farm a couple of years later, when Paul was half way through medical school.]

He met his wife, Melba, when he was at Concord, and they were married when he was at Concord. His wife graduated from Shady Springs High School, and she attended Concord also. She had two years of college, at Concord. They had their first child when he was a freshman at Kirksville. Sherry, the oldest one, was born in the college hospital at Kirksville.

Melba didn't go back to school after they were married. They started having a family, and she got her degree in, I believe, 1956, and he got his degree. He received his undergraduate degree the same year. He transferred his credits from the medical school to Concord.

Practicing in Pocahontas County

1962–2001

"Dr. Sharp was so kind, to everyone."
—Barbara McCarty, Dr. Sharp's longtime nurse

I came back to Frost for good in 1962. My son, Paul, liked Pocahontas County very much, so he told me about his second or third year in medical school, "Would you help me build a clinic in Green Bank?" And I, of course, said "Yes." He said, "That's where I'm going to start."

He graduated from Kirksville College of Osteopathic Medicine in 1958, completed an internship there, and came back to Green Bank for two years. We built a clinic for him at Green Bank in the summer of 1959 and he opened his office there on the 15th of September 1959. The weather was cold and bad, the two worst snowy years I can remember. He had to have a bulldozer plow the parking lot fifteen or twenty times that first winter. I've been here over thirty five years and have never had the office parking lot bulldozed even once. That winter the snow was piled as high as the roof of the building.

His oldest was just starting the first grade and his second child was born a week before the clinic was finished. He had a trailer moved in to live in. It was a very, very deluxe trailer at the end of the building so he could just step out and walk into the building. But the building had not been finished enough to really be a warm building. They did not have enough insulation in it. He thought, or we thought, that the winter would just be reasonable, but it was the worst winter I can remember. I came up to Pocahontas County when the children were sick a couple of times and stayed a week to relieve him. Then, they had the third child. They had the second one the week before he moved

Dr. Sharp's Green Bank office - photo taken in the early 1960s.

in the clinic in Green Bank, and a year later they had Melanie, the third one, in the hospital. She was the only one that was born here in Pocahontas County.

That winter that little Melanie was born, Melba had those three children. Two of them were babies. The little girl was six years old. He made house calls all over these mountains. I still have patients that come to me saying – "I went to Paul. Paul came way out around when the snow was knee deep." Just numerous ones. He never turned a call down. I think you have to love people, and love patients. If patients irritate you, don't practice medicine. And Paul was really liked. And I think that's one of the reasons that Melba really wanted or urged him to trade places. He just was out away from home so much, and her with those three little youngsters, it just got too much for her emotionally.

As soon as the second winter was over, his wife just said, "I can't stay here with these children in this cold." So, Paul said, "Why don't you and Opal come up here and stay in this office and let us live in your house in Mullens and I'll do the coal company office." [Back in Mullens] everybody that heard that, and the president of the local union said, "That's great. Any young doctor, he'll probably stay with us, you know."

What we had planned to do, after he got established, we were going to put two more rooms on, so we could work together. I knew he would be back. I was sure. I told him when he came here, "I'll probably supplement your income, because starting doctors don't get..." Oh, he did as well as I was doing in Mullens that first year. He did not have to have a nickel.

He went back to Mullens in 1961. And I went backwards and forwards for about six months to make sure that everything was stable with him in the company, and that he was able to do it. And, by that time, everybody was coming to him, and everybody that came in the office was asking for Paul instead of me. So, I felt pretty good. I got back up here, and I worked two days a week for awhile. I thought I might have to go back to

Mullens. Then, when things went real good, I decided that I would start full time here in Green Bank.

We switched offices and practices temporarily, but fate intervened and he departed this life in November of 1963, the day after John Kennedy was assassinated.

His wife said, "He got home late, about eleven. He sat down watching TV, drinking a Pepsi." And she said the kids were in bed. She was going to bed. And he said, "Well, I have a whole bunch of compensation, United Mine Worker files. I'm going to do some of these before I go to bed. And she said at three o'clock in the morning, the light was still on. And she yelled down, and he didn't answer, and she thought he was sleeping. She went down the stairs, and he was lying on the floor. She thought he was lying on the rug, taking a nap or going to sleep, and she walked over with her foot to push him and turn him over. When she put her foot on him, the lady that was staying with them said she screamed till you could hear her all over West Mullens Hill, "Something is wrong with Paul." And the lady jumped up and ran down there and they called the ambulance. And he had been dead an hour, an hour and half, maybe two hours. And it was such a shock, the doctor who was working in there really, Melba said, didn't do much of an examination or anything. He was so shook-up that the nurse did more than he in examining, and there was never any sign. So, they attributed it to cardiac arrest causing it.

He had been up here just a week or two before with the kids, for a day or two, and he was in great shape. And I do remember one thing, before he left, he give me a hug out here on the porch, and said "I sure am glad that you insisted I stay in school." He said, "I'm doing things for my kids that I never could have done." That's the way he left, which made me feel good, 'cause I always sort of felt that he may have gone on because I was encouraging him, since we didn't farm. That's about all I can say.

Paul's wife ultimately took the children back to Delaware, where she taught school. Opal and I would drive up there every holiday—Halloween, Thanksgiving, Christmas, Easter—and the girls would come and spend summers with us here in Frost. Melba has done really well with the kids.

Life Goes On

Since I was already living and practicing in Pocahontas County, I decided it would be better to stay here since we had the farm, the clinic, and my mother living in this area.

When I went up to Green Bank, I told the patients, "We're getting older. We're taking our vacations in the winter, sometimes for six or more weeks at a time. I want you to know before I become your doctor that I'm going to be away during part of the winter."

They all said that it didn't matter. "We'd rather have you for ten months than anyone else we know." That was really flattering. They're not only patients, they're friends. They're almost family. I've seen so many of these people pass away during recent years. I'm really getting worried. We don't have many old patients anymore. We see their children or grandchildren.

I spend a lot of time with my patients. Some doctors complain that "patients have been wasting a lot of my time" or "I've been petting the patient too much." I listen to their problems. Dr. Bernie Siegel of Yale University, a pediatrician and general surgeon, has said in his book that if the doctor will take the time to listen to the patient until the patient has finished, he will know what the trouble truly is. The patient will tell you what the problem is. I heard him lecture for five hours at a national convention. He gave numerous cases where he had seen patients who had been referred by good pediatricians. He said that if the referring doctor had just listened to the patient, the diagnosis would have been clear, but the doctor just didn't take the time to listen. He was a believer in the doctor talking to the patient about anything and everything. I tell patients stories so that they'll get comfortable with me. If they know you well, then they'll tell you what their problems are.

There was another professor of pediatrics I had and the students would gripe, "This guy doesn't teach anything." He was a clinical teacher who directed the students to go out into rural areas and make house calls to children. He said, "When you go into the child's house, look at the child. Pull up his clothes, look in his mouth, put the thermometer in his mouth, read the thermometer, look at the throat, look at the eyes, listen to the chest, and call me. If you haven't done one of those, I'll call somebody else. If you have done that, you can diagnose ninety five percent of all the children you look at." The students thought he wasn't teaching anything. After I got out in practice, I found that he really understood the fundamentals.

I think a doctor has to be able to talk about many different things with the patients because patients not only want to talk about their health, they want to be able to talk to you about family problems, about financial problems, and about other things that like that affect their general well-being. They talk to you about business problems, about their farm problems. To me, it's important that they get some advice or assurance, because if they're emotionally or mentally disturbed about problems, it will affect their medical health.

Symptoms and Sympathy

About half my office patients needed real treatment, and fifty percent of them just need comfort and assurance. That's really all. The others will have pain, cold, cough, skin problems, something like that, high blood pressure. Well, you talk about their problems. That's what you do most. You talk - you try to help them solve it. It'll be family problems, it'll be the children, the husband, the relatives, the neighbors, something like that, or it will be financial. You just talk about those things and try to suggest ways or various things they can do to change their environment, or to change their thinking so they won't be worrying. And the worry makes any little pain that you have, or anything that you have, worse. If you itch somewhere, if you're worried you're going to scratch it more, that's all.

And you had to have medicine for those who were worried. Back in those days, you could buy placebos. You could buy capsules that you could put sugar in, powdered sugar, or just whatever you wanted, or candy – anything. You could get any color you wanted. And you could always give a patient an aspirin. It's been proven, aspirin won't harm anyone if they are not allergic to it, and it may help a majority of people. And aspirin was made in a pink, and yellow, and green, and white-modeled color, so you could change medicines anytime you wanted.

Well, if I thought they came for the pill, I gave it to them. You could tell when you talked to them a little bit whether your talk was helping, because, if it was, they would immediately tell you, "I'm going to try what you're telling me, " or something. If they didn't do that, then they got the pink one.

What I did when I gave the pink was to give the best first, because everyone liked the pink one. If you laid them out in your hand and asked them to take a pill of their choice, they're all alike. Four out of five will take the pink one. I've tried that.

I only had a few patients that came more than they should. It was because of worry. They had a heart problem, or hypertension. And every time their heart fluttered, or they felt the pulse was fast, or their head hurt a little, they ran in to have their blood pressure taken. Now, I have tried to get through patients' head, over and over, that I never knew hypertension or high blood pressure to cause headache in anyone. And many of them come, and you say, "Are you taking your heart medicine regular, just like the directions; especially, your blood pressure?" "No. I take it pretty regular, but really I take it as often as I need it." And I always tried to get across, "You cannot tell when you need heart medicine. You have no idea when you need high blood pressure-".

"Well, I know when I feel bad and I need it." And my answer is, "There is no earthly way, when you feel bad, it may be sky-high. The day you feel best, it could be high. That may be why you're feeling so good, because it can go to both ends. It can make your feelings like either end of the spectrum." But some patients still insist. My sister-in-law was one who said, "You can't tell me that – I can tell every time."

I see most of my patients in my office. I don't ask them for money. I never did. I never sent them bills. They pay me when they can. My collections have always been better than any of my colleagues I talk to.

Faith, Family, and Health

My family were regular churchgoers. My grandfather Sharp and a cousin built the original Frost Methodist Church. It burned in the sixties. I went to that church every Sunday until I grew up and got married. After that I went to the Presbyterian Church. That's what happens when you get married. I'm a believer. I'm not a radical. I have members of my family in every church. I even have one who converted to Judaism. I'm tolerant of all of them.

I used to tell the medical students, "I don't care what faith, what religion, you have, but I believe it is essential for a physician to have some type of faith." I think you have a physical body, a mental body, and a spiritual body. If you read *Time* magazine or *Newsweek,* they have been writing about what is necessary for good health and spirituality is one of the important contributors to good health. I think that is important for the patient's health. If you're ill, you have to deal with that. If the physician is not in a position to discuss that in some way, or let you talk to him, he's not treating the whole person. I don't think you'll be burnt out if you have faith yourself. A faith of some sort is basic.

I really don't minister to people who are facing death. I let them talk to me. I ask them sometimes, "How do you feel about it? Do you have faith of any sort?" I like them to tell me whether they do or not. If they do have faith, I don't think the patient ever really gives up. They're willing to try, to do anything you tell them. They follow any guidance you give them more freely. In these articles that I've mentioned, they've been unable to explain why patients who have been told they have little chance recovery still believe in their hearts that they may get better. The patient says, "Do you think I can?" And you say, "It's possible," and sometimes they do recover. There is a point when I say, "There's nothing I can do." But if you have the faith, it is possible to recover.

What experts now seem to think may happen is that your brain metabolism is actually altered. Your mental ability and metabolic function change all the time, even in small ways. If someone walks up behind you and says "BOO!" your urinary tract, your digestion, everything is altered for several minutes. In some people metabolic function can be altered for hours. That's why I don't go for practical jokes like that.

Emergencies

One of the emergencies we had was a little girl who let her bicycle get away on a hill, and fell off, and all her front teeth were loose. And she had cuts all over the face, and it took us about an hour, or an hour and half here on the porch to get her wounds sewed up and her teeth pushed back properly. And in the meantime, we had called Dr. Mallow, the dentist in Marlinton, and asked if he would check her. And when they finished here, they took her to Dr. Mallow, and he adjusted the teeth in the sockets - put a brace or something. She ended up with all good teeth, with the exception of one.

There were not very many farm accidents. The only things we had in the way of farm accidents would be chainsaw accidents. One little farm accident that was simple looking could have been fatal. H.A. Taylor, Henry's boy, when he was ten years old – ten to twelve – he was helping his dad make hay. They had a load

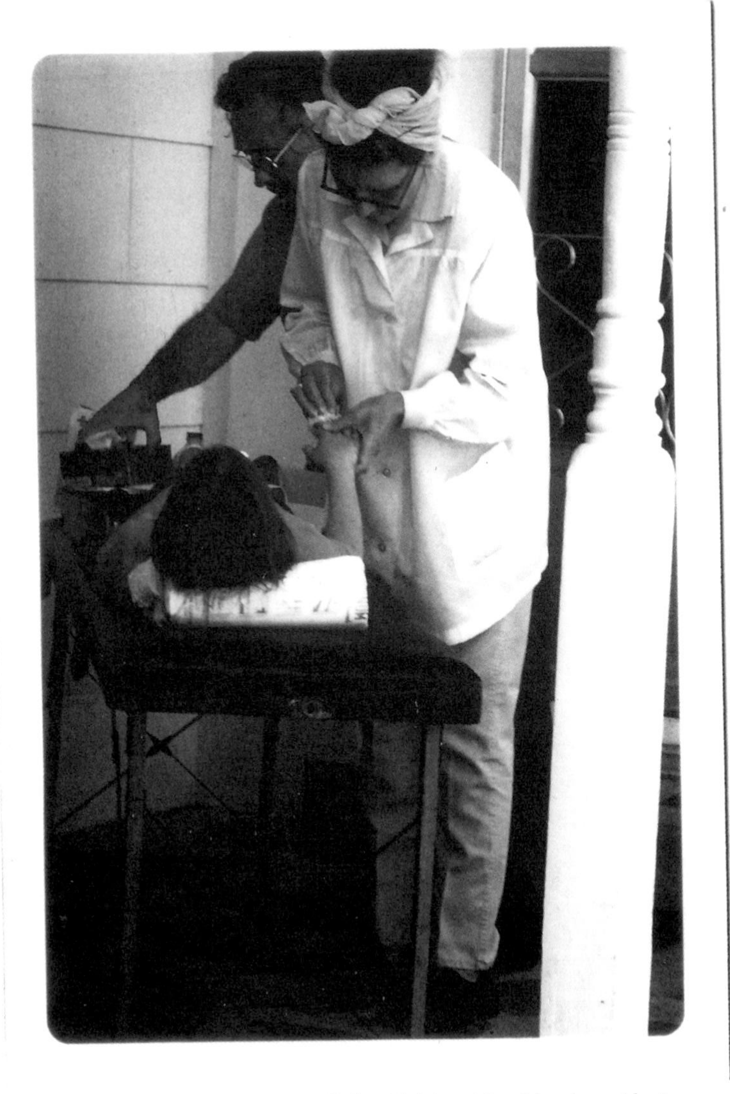

Opal and Dr. Sharp treating a little girl, injured in a bicycle accident, in his "front porch emergency room."

of bales on a hay wagon, and his dad was bringing the tractor to hook up to the hay bales. It was on a hillside, and H.A. wanted to help. He was the one who was going to put the pin in when Henry backed in, but H.A. just straddled the tongue, and picked the tongue up as Henry was coming. He didn't wait. And the wagon took off down the hill. And H.A. was sitting on that tongue. It ran all the way down that hill. Finally shook him off, but he didn't have a fracture. But the inside of his legs, all the way down, where it slammed and shook him around, just turned as black as your shirt.

I remember one of the auto accidents that was totally left to me. And I could have sent this patient to the hospital. But, if I had sent him to the hospital, they would have just called me to the hospital, because, at that time, I was the only doctor on the staff that they could get out at night. There would be some excuse from the others. So, we kept him at the office at Green Bank. This injured man was in a Chevrolet with a heavy load in the back, a station wagon. He had a heavy load of electrical equipment for the Observatory. His name was Robert E. Lee. He was going around the curve, the first curve right above the bridge at Dunmore. It was a real sharp curve. He ran into that curve too fast and ran right straight out over the road and hit the bank. He hit so hard that the hood of his car turned up toward the windshield, came right through the windshield and hit him in the face. It hit him in the mouth and knocked the teeth loose and cut one side of his mouth open, clear to the ear. I said, "Either go to the hospital and fix him, or - " They brought him to the office. So, when we got to the office, a man came in and told me, "I think you need some help. I was an army medic. I can at least hand you some things. I can help you, if you've got to fix him here." I told the people that brought him, "I'd just as well do it here. I have the equipment." So, he was conscious. When you asked him, "Open your mouth like that," you would see all down the throat, look at all the teeth, clear behind the teeth on both sides. So, I had to go inside and had to suture the mucous membrane right out to the front, then go back and do the outside. Then, his minor wounds we took care of. There were several of those. Plus a fracture someplace on the face; the cheek bone.

But after a couple of hours, I sent him on to the hospital. I called the company that he was working for, and they said that would be a Workman's Compensation case. He was from North Carolina, and it would be all right. They asked me first if he could be sent home. And I said I didn't think so. He should be left until we saw if there would be any post surgical infection. So, they agreed.

And the man got along great. We released him just as quickly as we could get the sutures out, or get most of them out, and was sure that there would be no infection, discharged him to go back there. I heard from him a time or two. About a year later, someone tapped on the door. I went to the door. He looked at me and said, "Do you remember me?" I said, "Faintly." I said, "Robert E. Lee." Nobody would forget. He said, "Look at my face. You can hardly see a scar," and it had been open clear to the ear. That was one of my best, but one of my most serious. He had a fracture in the face. He had some other minor fractures – chest. But, other than that, I think things went well.

Taking a Chance

There was only thing that I ever did in the office that I didn't feel that I was qualified to do, but I just felt that it was a necessity. The patient was a little girl, and only about ten years old. She developed a cyst, a tumor, in the corner of her eye. There wasn't any insurance or money to take her to the hospital. There was a little bit of welfare or something back then, but that was before Medicare or Medicaid, anything like that got started, and there must have been a dozen kids in that family.

This cyst got bigger and bigger as the months went by, until it was almost the size of a ping-pong ball. It had just pushed the eye over, 'til the eye was useless. And the family said, "We can't take her to a specialist. We don't have the money to take her anywhere." The kids called her "Punkin' Eye," in school, and things got worse. And I finally said, "Bring her in here." I knew it wasn't malignant. I said, "Bring her in. We'll do something. We'll try to take that out of there. But I want you to know, I have never done surgery around the eye - I have taken tumors that size off of the body, but nothing around the eye." So, they brought her in. It took about an hour, hour and a quarter, and we got the whole cyst out, intact, without rupturing it. And I sutured it. The thing, when you do work like that, you have to have sutures that are just like hair almost, in size. I didn't have any that small. But, anyway I had sutures that worked pretty well, in the end.

When she came back for a visit, another doctor, a student doctor was there, and I would say I had student doctors practically all the time. That was before the time of the school in Lewisburg. They came from medical schools here and there across the country. Anyway, when that child came in, her face was black, clear down. She was black clear down the body and was I scared. And this boy who was with me wanted to know "What's the trouble? What causes that?" I said, "Your face, and around your eye, is the most vascular place in the body." And what happened, I didn't get some of those little blood vessels tied off, or cauterized, and they continued to bleed, and just filtered down for the next day or two, through the soft tissue, even out in the shoulder. Well, anyway, it had quit by the time I saw her. And I assured the boy, "When she comes back, she'll be a lot better." Sure enough, she was. And about two weeks, that kid's eye was about as nice as the other one. And you look at it today and you won't be able, I believe, to ever tell that she had a cyst. That's the only thing that I ever did that I wasn't trained to do. The mistake too many doctors make is doing things that they're not trained to do.

Working in the Hospital

When I came back to Pocahontas County, Mr. Cochran – Clyde Cochran – was administrator, or business manager, of the hospital and he immediately wanted me to apply for staff privileges. And he said, "Nobody from the upper end of the county has ever been on the staff. They just wouldn't come – drive that far. Since you live part of the way, we need you, we've got to have you"

You know, he really was putting the pressure on. So, I did. And in early, I believe, '63, I became a staff member, and I remained a staff member until I retired, even though the last few years I only took courtesy privileges, because, after seventy five, they didn't require you to cover at night. There were no emergency room doctors as such. When somebody came in that was an emergency, the nurse called the doctor. If he couldn't give her information over the phone, he had to go in, and they took turn about. But the two doctors they had here in 1963 just didn't go. They both had real problems, and I didn't really know what was going on when I agreed to take call. And, what happened, after I become a staff member, I was going to the hospital four and five times a night.

I delivered three out of every five babies that came in there for two or three years. I delivered babies for women that I'd never seen before. The other doctors would do checkups, and take the case, but when the nurse called for the delivery, she couldn't find them. Mrs. Eula Gibson [the head nurse] did more deliveries than most of the doctors before I came, and she drew a big breath and said, "Boy am I glad to see someone that comes at night. I have to come every other night when I'm not on duty." She was a good mid-wife.

An Emergency Room at Home

I also saw patients here at my house. We had lots of patients come here, but they were always at night. And I had so many

Dr. Sharp's home, Willow Lane Farm, just south of Frost, in Pocahontas County WV. The willows along the lane had not yet been planted in this photo from the 1950's.

calls at night that I just told my wife – we were having the house repaired – "I'm going to put a little room on the end of the house, and they can come up out there. They won't be beating on our door and coming in." So, we put that room in there; put a table, surgical tray, and all of it. I sewed up heads here at the house, hands, accidents. I put shoulders and hips in place. The most of the dislocations were boys that were playing ball. That would be at night. Before, I was having to go to the hospital for minor things like that – put a shoulder back. So, I did that in here.

Believe it or not, most of the heads I sewed up back in those days were put there by the police, because police were a lot different in those days. The ones they had up at Durbin or Cass, those were pretty rough places. And if a guy got a little bit unruly, he got clouted over the head, and I even had State Police customers in this place that had really got mean out along the highway somewhere. Times have changed.

We didn't see colds. I just wouldn't see colds and take peoples' blood pressure at night or anything like that. When they would call, we would just tell them, "You'll have to come to the office. This is strictly for an emergency. I have nothing here to give you." Oh, I would see them if someone had a child with a temperature of 103 or 104. And that would save them time, if they were from Marlinton and would have to go to Green Bank. Rather than them run up there to the clinic, I would say, "You run to the house today. Go to the door on the side and I will give your youngster an antibiotic."

Opal Passes Away

Opal passed away in 1978, three months before the first class in the new medical school graduated. Opal had enjoyed excellent health all her life. And she was like so many people, she always thought if she felt bad, "Sooner or later my heart - It will be my heart. That goes in our family." And her fatality was from ovarian cancer, which is the most untreatable and the most insidious cancer that women can have. It was never diagnosed, I don't believe, until the patient was terminal.

The last year was unbelievably hard. She had her surgery in Florida, where I had training in anesthesiology. And the hospital that took all of our first class of students, she decided that's where she would go before it was diagnosed. It was diagnosed as a uterine fibroid. So, she said, "That's where I'll go for surgery." And they when they opened her up, one of the surgeons came out "We have bad news. It's ovarian cancer, and it's all over the peritoneum. There is no use in any surgery. We're closing. So, on to radiation. I think she had sixty-five treatments in a year and a half, all that she possibly could have. That's the only thing that lengthened her life. Chemotherapy did no good. Every three weeks, until she passed away, I took her to Richmond for treatment. And I can see it was not doing any good. Each time she would be sicker. Then she would start improving, and she always said, about the middle of the third week, "I'm not going back." But when the day came, she always went back. That's where she passed away. She had a treatment one day and died forty-eight hours following.

Opal had a real sense of loyalty, that was one, her moral and ethical actions, and her kindness towards people, her thoughtfulness, and a real feeling that she wanted to be of help to me and a help to anyone that came in. And she was totally devoid of working for money.

One of my inherited characteristics is "Do all you can do for anybody, or everybody, regardless of their station in life, and don't question what you will get out of it." I learned that from my parents, and she may have gotten it from hers. I don't know. But my dad always said, "Give a little more than you expect."

Philosophically, Opal and I were totally together. There was never any argument or confusion, or anything concerning our working together. There was no way that I could express our life together, really. It was totally together. The first part of it was maybe tempestuous, like all early marriages when you're a youngster, and when you're trying to prepare a place to live, that was the only time we ever had any arguments. It was about where we would live, or where we would stay, or something like that, because she didn't like having to live with my parents, even though she loved me. After we were married, she had a feeling; after you're married, you were everything to your husband. And she looked at me always and said, "You're everything to me. I'm first, and you're first."

All of these, any awards I have, I've appreciated, but I don't really think I've earned it. This is what she always said - Every once in awhile, if she was a little fussy or complained, I would say, "Well, I don't do this. I don't smoke. I don't drink. I stay at home at night. I don't see other women." You know, things that you would say if you're bad or not. She always stood and looked at me, "Do you really think that you should be honored for things that you ought to do?" And she looked so serious when she would say that. "You did a good deed. Do you think you ought to be honored? That's what's expected of us." And she said that so much to me that I learned to believe it. I just think other people pushed me and she was one of them.

She was one of the greatest ladies that I ever had the privilege of knowing in any way.

The World Changing: Capstone for a Century of Living

I well remember Pearl Harbor. I was in my second year of medical school and that changed the world forever. Before then, people were living totally different lives, much more complacent, quiet, reserved. After Pearl Harbor, everything took off—the explosion of technology and growth changed the world forever.

There's been more change in the last half of the twentieth century than there has been in the whole nineteen centuries before. Medicine, science, and everything. I guess people at the turn of the century couldn't see how it could advance any faster, but I have lived in a century that began with no automobiles and has ended with airplanes that can go 2100 miles per hour, traversing our country in less than two hours.

Consider me going to Marlinton on my first trip, over mud roads in a buggy and not seeing a single automobile. Then consider me hopping on a plane the way we do now, going to Pensacola, Florida to see my wife's son and getting there in two hours from our airport in Lewisburg. You can cross the Atlantic [by airplane]. Most of my grandchildren have been in Europe, half a dozen countries. I have a great-grandson who just came back from Germany. He knows the subways in London better than he knows them in New York. I remember the little old roads that went down through here, the towns around here that used to be thriving and now have shrunk up to just about nothing.

I don't see that I could have lived any time before or after we'd witness that much change. I was a middle-aged man by the time they landed on the moon. They'll be somebody on Mars soon. I see the rationale for preparing for those projects because we develop things that are used in all types of sciences - medicine, agriculture, everything like that.

Those are things to look forward to, but I don't think we'll ever establish colonies on Mars or even the moon. There are a few laws of nature that you can't break - those include the speed of sound, of electricity, and of light. If we can't change those things, then we can never explore other planets because of the distance. Other than Mars, I don't know one that any person would want to get to. How long does it take to get to Mars? Three months, or something like that. Venus and Jupiter or one of those would be so many lifetimes away that you wouldn't get there unless human life could be extended indefinitely. That's the only hope. I don't think that's possible with the current human frame. If you were able to regenerate cells and organs, you might be able to extend lifespan significantly. If you could change the chromosome pattern, change the genes, and replace the aging genes with growing ones, you might be able to do something like that.

I have read where someday the world will speak English. Have you read that? I've read it, but I heard it on TV the other day, on one of these quiz shows. The question was, "What is the most extensively spoken language in the world today?" and immediately I said, "Chinese." And the answer was English. I thought it would be Chinese or Hindu. The answer to that is that those countries don't all speak the same language. They have so many languages and dialects that when you break it down, English emerges as the dominant language. French is the second most extensively spoken language. The next thing they said is that English controls the industrial world. Not only did I read that, the same time they said the dollar will one day be the world's medium of exchange. All of the world's industry speaks English and trades in the dollar.

The Medical School That Was Meant to Be

1972–1978

"When we first started, the mission of this institution was to train primary care physicians for rural Appalachia and West Virginia, and that need is still critical...It was a national need, and to some extent, in terms of primary care physicians, it's still a crisis situation."

- Fred Smith, one of the founders of WVSOM

-

This chapter has been compiled from interviews with Roland Sharp in the fall of 2001 and from a presentation in March 1991 by Fredric W. Smith, Executive Vice President of the West Virginia School of Osteopathic Medicine, to a group of WVSOM students. Dr. Sharp and Mr. Smith worked closely together to help found WVSOM. The narrative here alternates between these two oral histories to construct an imaginary conversation between the two men, co-workers and longtime friends. Fred Smith passed away in 1996.

FRED SMITH: *I was thinking about what would be a good theme for this history and what I came up with was "The medical school that was meant to be." When you think of all the obstacles that we've faced, not only legislatively, but just in starting up and getting approval for the school, most people would lay heavy odds against this school's ever surviving. When I think back through all those hurdles and crises we faced it's amazing to me, just on a percentage basis, we have made it. And then when I think about why we could make it under such circumstances, it becomes pretty obvious* *why we overcame these obstacles. Our purpose—the mission of this institution from the beginning—was to train primary care physicians for rural Appalachia and West Virginia, and that need is still critical. It's a crying need. When we first started this school it was a national need, and to some extent, in terms of primary care physicians, it's still a crisis situation.*

An Empty Building Finds a Purpose

ROLAND SHARP: Well, in the late sixties, the Appalachian Regional Commission was formed. All the Appalachian states were members and each had a board of directors. I don't know how many were on the board of directors in West Virginia, but it represented several professions. Dr. Frank Wallington of Moundsville was our D.O., Doctor of Osteopathic Medicine, representative. The West Virginia board met monthly in various areas of West Virginia, but most of the time it was at Morgantown, at the university [WVU].

In 1972 Dr. Wallington was at a meeting in Morgantown and someone came to the meeting from the Greenbrier Military School, in Lewisburg, WV, which had just closed. He offered to sell the entire institution, with forty seven acres of land, to anyone who could use it, preferably for an educational institution, for $500,000. That price was ridiculous and I believe that the reason the price was so low was that they probably had, through the Internal Revenue Service, depreciated the value down to that.

The owners of the school, the Moore family, wanted the campus to continue as some type of educational facility. I think they would have settled for its being used for a hospital or something like that, but it had to be something that would be useful to the community. Not a soul was interested. The military schools were going out all over the country because the generation of students through the sixties had made army, navy, and war all bad words. They just weren't getting applicants. The second thing was the Moore family members were getting older, with only one young member. I think the one was Dr. Houston Moore, who later went to medical school.

But even though they offered that institution at a very low price, nobody said anything. Dr. Wallington sat there thinking. Finally, he got a bright idea, "I think we ought to buy it, the West Virginia Society of Osteopathic Medicine." So he got in touch with the GMS representative and asked if he could have an option and how much it would cost for an option for sixty days or six months, I can't remember exactly which. The Moore family's representative said, "$10,000" and Dr. Wallington said, "OK, we'll take it." Dr. Wallington came back immediately and called the president of our state osteopathic society and asked him to have a meeting to see if there were enough doctors to put up the money for the option.

Frank's idea was to establish a school of osteopathic medicine. He went back home and called about ten or fifteen doctors and asked them to come to Charleston for a meeting. I went to Charleston and he told the story and said, "I promised them $10,000. I don't have the money, but I called you all to see who would be willing to contribute." Well, everyone there was willing to contribute. When he told us what he was planning, not very many of us, including myself, thought that the idea would fly. But he said, "The price is so cheap!" He said, "It's such a good deal that if we bought it, we could make a million dollars if we turn it into a school."

So, ten or twelve of the doctors there said, "We'll put up a thousand dollars." The $10,000 for the option actually came from the state osteopathic society, but we pledged our money to reimburse the society in case the project failed. So Dr. Wallington collected the money, went back to the Moore family in Lewisburg, and paid the fee for the option.

I was willing to put up the money because it was worth probably five million as a financial investment. Dr. Wallington thought the medical school was a good idea because there weren't nearly enough family doctors in West Virginia. We were sold—enough that we put the money up! Dr. Wallington was a smart person and a fast talker. He could sell you on about anything. He graduated from medical school in Philadelphia and had also graduated from West Virginia University. The major pitch was, "Give me a good reason why we can't. We need it. West Virginia University [WVU] medical students are all specializing and they're all leaving the state." Marshall University didn't have a medical school then. He said, "We could have the best GP [general practitioner] school in the country. And where could we get such a physical plant all ready to start out in?"

The Founders

FRED SMITH: *The four physicians whom the state society recognized to come to Lewisburg and talk to the Moore family became known as the founders of the West Virginia School of Osteopathic Medicine. Dr. Frank Wallington was from Moundsville, a GP who has been deceased for a number of years now. Dr. Carlton Apgar came from Huntington. He is still living and practicing medicine, and two of his sons who graduated from this school are practicing medicine with him now. Dr. Don Newell, Sr., from Oak Hill, was a founder. His son practices with him but graduated from Kirksville College of Osteopathic Medicine, I believe. He has been on our advisory boards and clinic boards. And finally, Dr. O.J. Bailes, who practiced in Princeton [West Virginia], came here, became a part of our administration and faculty, and left here and ended up in Pomona, California as the dean of the school there [Western University of Health Sciences]. He retired from that and came back here. He is now practicing in Princeton and sits on our clinic board.*

There was one other person a lot of people still call a founder, but really was not as instrumental, and that was Dr. Alexander Trefz from Weston. I think he had delivered 5,000 babies in Weston. Just a remarkable man. While he wasn't a founder, he was a critical player in the state society and as a physician in starting this school. [There were times] we were ready to close up because we couldn't pay bills. That's

Early days at the school in Lewisburg. From Left - Founder Dr. Jerry Bailes, Dr. Sharp, and Fred Smith. Photo courtesy of the West Virginia School of Osteopathic Medicine.

before we ever opened the doors. Dr. Trefz loaned us money at a very reasonable interest with no strings attached as to when we had to pay it back. This helped us pay our bills and keep things moving here so that we could complete our feasibility study and move ahead.

The Other Players

ROLAND SHARP: Then the next thing they did was try to get people interested in Lewisburg. There were two of us—Dr. [A. Robert] Dzmura of Weirton and me—who were the only two osteopathic doctors in the state who had had experience teaching in a medical school. Dr. Dzmura had been an anatomy instructor at the osteopathic college at Des Moines University, and I had been in three departments at the Kirksville school during the war. They had used both of us in various capacities because there was a real shortage of teachers. Well, Dr. Dzmura said, "I have five or six children and I live in Weirton. So it's almost impossible for me to commute down. I think since you're close, you should volunteer to do this."

And several of the others said, "Well, since you're close, we'd like for you to do it."

Since I didn't know it couldn't be done I said, "Okay, I will do the best I can."

I couldn't be in the group of four doctors who first chartered the school because I was an employee. They appointed me dean long before we were accredited, so I was the guy who carried the ball trying to get accreditation. I couldn't serve on the board. I become acting dean at the end of 1972. I didn't live in Lewisburg or go down there every day. I just made the trips from here at home in Frost. I worked with the other people we had there.

Dr. Jerry Bailes, a founder from Princeton, was very much interested and put some money up. He commuted from Princeton to Lewisburg and was willing to assist in any way he could.

Dr. Bailes scouted around Concord College to see if he could find someone there who knew something about federal grants or advanced faculty recruiting. Dr. Bailes knew that Dr. Elizabeth Blatt was not employed and he told me about it. Dr. Blatt was a Smith College graduate with a Ph.D. in physiology from Union College. Her husband was at Concord College in the biology department. She was also at the Concord biology department, but back about that time, in 1972, the state college enrollment went down in West Virginia, so Dr. Blatt was dropped temporarily from the faculty. She was very, very skilled at writing grants. I asked [Dr. Bailes] to stop and talk to her about doing some work with us. She was just happy to be working or doing something. She came up from Concord and talked with me. I am a Concord graduate and had been president of the Concord Alumni Association, so I knew a lot of people she knew down there. As a matter of fact, I went to college with Billy L. Coffindaffer, who was president of Concord at the time. He and I were friends, and he and Governor [Arch A.] Moore were good friends, and he sent everyone he thought could be of help up to us.

I knew Fred Smith very well here in Pocahontas County—belonged to the Rotary Club with Fred. I talked to Fred about it. Fred Smith was principal of the high school in Pocahontas County. He was also a member of the advisory committee of the North Central Accrediting Agency and he knew a lot about accreditation. His family were my patients. We'd talk about it and occasionally I'd ask him, "Can you help me out with this?" He'd run over to my house, or I'd run over to his house. Pretty soon we were going to Lewisburg together on Saturdays and Sundays.

So we had Dr. Blatt from Concord College and Fred Smith from Pocahontas County, and then we got Sue Keller. I knew Sue Keller very well. When she moved to Pocahontas County, she and her husband were patients of mine at Green Bank. She had a master's degree in clinical pathology from WVU and was the laboratory technician at the hospital in Marlinton. At that time they had one of the best laboratories in the state because she was a highly competent lady. I talked to her. Sue said, "I would be willing. I'll help you all as much as I can." She was way above a medical technician and she knew how to write grants.

Sue Keller and Dr. Blatt would meet down in Lewisburg two or three days a week. Sue's work at the hospital could be completed in an hour or two in the morning and then she had the day free. I volunteered my time and Sue, Dr. Blatt, and Fred all volunteered their time until we later had money for some back pay. We took those positions with the knowledge that we might never get anything.

The business manager at Concord came up when we needed assistance, free of charge. He'd drive up from Athens, [WV], spend the day, and work on the budget. We all worked for free because we loved the idea. It was great. It was really something! Fred Smith had six children and he gave up the principalship of the high school in Pocahontas County as soon as we became a state school and he could be guaranteed a salary. However, there were no guarantees that the institution would remain accredited. He took the chance anyway. He was vice president when he died.

FRED SMITH: *Those founding physicians came down to Lewisburg in the spring of 1972. I lived in Pocahontas County at the time, and Dr. Roland Sharp, who became our first president, asked me to help when I saw him at a Rotary Ladies Night dinner. I didn't know anything about osteopathic medicine, but he was my family physician at the time. He was a good doctor, and he was my doctor, and that's all I knew and all I cared about. He said that they were coming down to Lewisburg in a couple of weeks to talk to the Moore family and to meet with [U.S.] Senator [Robert C.] Byrd, [U.S.] Senator [Jennings] Randolph, Congressman [Harley O.] Staggers, and State Senator Ralph Williams to talk about this. They were also planning to attend the groundbreaking ceremony for the Greenbrier Valley Hospital. He wanted to know if I would come down to Lewisburg and talk with them, and maybe assist them. He knew my background in education administration, accreditation and grants work. He wondered if I would talk to the founders, and see how I felt about assisting them with some of those efforts, specifically a feasibility study and getting some start-up grants.*

So I did come down with Dr. Sharp. At that point we proceeded to develop a nonprofit corporation and made application to the Appalachian Regional Commission headquartered in Washington, D.C. I made a visit over there because the founders had had an application, but they didn't know what to do with it, and they had let the deadline lapse. I called them [the ARC], went over and visited, and got an extension on the application. I filled out the grant application, which gave us about $166,000 to do a feasibility study, a requirement to get accreditation from the Committee on Colleges of the American Osteopathic Association. I coordinated the process, but I didn't do it all. There were a lot of people who assisted; Dr. Blatt, Sue Keller, and Dr. Sharp. We would meet in Lewisburg regularly and do the work on the feasibility study. It showed that we had the financial resources to be able to start the school. We had to develop the curriculum and we had to show that we had the capability of attracting an entering class, a student body, which was easy because there was such a big demand.

The Battle for Accreditation

ROLAND SHARP: Then Dr. Wallington started the process of trying to collect money to establish a school. The governor [Arch Moore] told us immediately that we were assured $500,000 in Appalachian Regional [Commission] funds, which was enough to pay for the property, but he couldn't give it to us until we opened. Our congressman, Harley Staggers, said that if we filed the proper application, he could probably get us something like $1,300,000 of Hill-Burton funds to renovate the facilities, because there was plenty of money then for colleges and especially medical schools[5].

[5] The Hospital Survey and Construction Act of 1946, informally known as the Hill-Burton Act, allocated federal grants and guaranteed loans to the states to improve health care facilities. The Act required facilities that received funding to provide a reasonable volume of services to persons unable to pay and to make their services available to all persons residing in the facility's area.

Immediately, Dr. Wallington and Dr. Apgar started looking for somewhere to borrow the money to purchase the school until the governor could give us the $500,000 after we opened. First Century Bank in Huntington immediately offered to let the state osteopathic society have the money because they looked at it like this, I guess, "If they don't make their goal, we get a real deal here because they put the institution up as collateral. And it's certainly worth a lot more than $500,000!"

The only holdup was that Dr. Wallington didn't know too much about setting up a school. He was not well grounded in education or in education administration. He wanted to start the medical school right then, that fall, but those of us who knew some more about it knew that you could not open an osteopathic medical school without pre-accreditation status from the American Association of Colleges of Osteopathic Medicine. At that time unless you graduated from an accredited medical school, you couldn't be licensed to practice medicine in forty six of the fifty states!

To start with, Dr. Wallington announced to the press that we were going to take a class in the fall of 1972. Well, the accrediting body, when they read that, immediately called and said, "Whose idea is this? You're not going to start any medical school. We're not going to permit it."

So we had almost two years of negotiating with the Committee on Colleges of the American Osteopathic Association, which was the only body that could accredit an osteopathic school of medicine, and those were tough characters. Sure, they wanted to see more osteopathic schools open, but they said, "In the first place, you don't have the money. In the second place, the town is too little. You can't get faculty to come and live in a little place like this[6]. They wouldn't stay overnight. The third thing is that you can't run a school on a million dollars."

We had Senator Randolph and Senator Byrd at Lewisburg for a meeting in late 1972 or early 1973. We also had a couple of

---

[6] Lewisburg's population was under 4,000 at that time.

members of the accrediting board there, and we had a professor from the Michigan State University College of Osteopathic Medicine giving us guidance. Our big stumbling block was the accrediting commission.

Governor Moore told us, "No problem there. If you get accreditation, we will see that it is a state school and you have the funds you need."

So it was chartered in December 1972 as the Greenbrier College of Osteopathic Medicine and it was still named that when we took the first class. The first class entered in October of 1974. It was late because the accrediting body did not get to the place where they would grant us temporary accreditation until fall 1974.

Fred Smith: *So we did that feasibility study and we presented it to the Committee on Colleges of the American Osteopathic Association. It was a real battle, because we were the seventh or eighth school of osteopathic medicine. There are fifteen or sixteen now [in 1991]. We came in behind Texas. Texas had started a school which had had a lot of difficulty and the Committee on Colleges was very concerned about that. They didn't want to have another Texas situation. Our situation on the surface, well actually in reality, was real shaky and they could see that. We had that obstacle and there were members on the Committee on Colleges who did not want us to start up. We had a real battle. We traveled all over the country to meet with the Committee on Colleges - Boston, Minneapolis, Washington, Chicago, Dallas, and Michigan State University. We finally convinced them that we met all their requirements.*

There was a little bluffing that was going on there. I have to tell this story on Dr. Roland Sharp. There was a requirement that we had to show proof of $500,000 in the bank to start up. Well, that was a lot of money. Today it doesn't seem like that much, but in 1972 that was a lot of money. Dr. Sharp always took his checkbook, and when they'd talk about it, he said, "We've got it. We've got the money. Here's my checkbook." And there was nothing in it! And that's the truth. I mean I was there, I saw that happen all the time. I was amazed that *they didn't do a little more research on that and check with the bank and ask, "Really, do you have $500,000 in the bank?" The Committee on Colleges came here and made a lot of visits between 1972 and 1974.*

ROLAND SHARP: So it was meeting after meeting [with the accreditation committee]. Fred and I traveled all over, and they came to the institution and looked it over time and again. They appointed two doctors—a Ph.D. and another doctor who was vice-provost for medical affairs, both from Ohio State University—to come take a look. Then they appointed the past president of the Chicago College of Osteopathic Medicine, Richard N. MacBain. He had been president of that college from 1938 to 1967 and had retired to North Carolina. He was available and he was highly respected in the medical profession. They had him come as one of the advisory members.

Believe it or not, all three of those advisory members thought the school was a good idea because our idea of establishing a medical school to train family physicians was considerably different from what people establishing medical schools in the past had done. All they had been trying to see was who had the largest and the best hospitals, and who had the most research. Our idea was to forget about hospitals and about research until we got going well and had trained some family physicians for the state. There were plenty of counties in West Virginia back at that time that had just one or two doctors.

We met in Kansas City and Dr. MacBain made a dramatic speech before that accrediting committee. They didn't let us sit in on the meeting, but we heard about it later. Some of our friends were eavesdropping, I think. He just told that accrediting body, "If you turn that group down in West Virginia, you are killing the best chance for a medical school that I've seen in the past twenty five years."

Several people gave us a favorable recommendation. Dr. Richard Meiling, who was an M.D. in gynecological surgery and pathology both, was a nationally known figure. He was hired by the Board of Regents to evaluate our prospects. He held a press conference after he visited our school for nearly three days and said, "This institution is super." He couldn't believe what a fine physical plant we had. Most schools start in one room or an old discarded building. Here we have this huge complex, two gymnasiums, and an intact library. When Dr. Meiling went to Charleston, he found that *The Charleston Gazette* was very much against us, but the [Charleston] *Daily Mail* evidently had representatives on our side. He told the newspapers that the institution was really superb and that he had reviewed the people we had secured for faculty and everyone was top notch. We had everything and it would be an error if they passed up the opportunity to let the school open. He said, "It's great. They're ready to go. I've looked over their faculty prospects and they're as good as any in the country. As far as I'm concerned, they're ready to go now." Later people said, "The Board of Regents hired him to put the school down, but he put it into orbit!"

The Charleston Gazette was so much against the school; they didn't come to his press conference. The *Daily Mail* printed it. The *Gazette* was totally against it. The *Gazette* is 100 percent for WVU and the *Gazette* has been mad ever since the university medical school became a four-year school that it wasn't put in Charleston instead of Morgantown. The *Gazette* believes that WVU Medical School should be right in Charleston. They didn't want any more medical schools in West Virginia. They said, "One's plenty for a little state like this. It's too expensive." They thought we were going to build a big hospital down here. I didn't even waste my time talking to them about it. When the folks at the *Gazette* get something in their heads, they're cut and dried and set. You would have to switch out the entire editorial staff to change their minds.

After that dramatic speech and after the press conference in Charleston, the accrediting body finally made a decision. So we were at the Kansas City meeting in early '74, and one of them said to me, "Well, we're gonna let y'all go. I bet you fifty-fifty that you don't make it." And he walked off.

Going Public

Fred Smith: *We started in 1974 and we could see that we had to make a decision very quickly whether to remain private and double our tuition to survive, or to try to go to the state and get state support. We debated on that for some time. Obviously the decision was, "Let's see if we can become a state institution." The reason for that was that we didn't want to change the mission of our school. If we had doubled our tuition, it would have deprived a lot of students from West Virginia and the Appalachian region of the opportunity to go to medical school. These potential students were very bright, capable people, but they often lacked the financial resources to go to a private school. If we chose to stay private and double the tuition, most of our students, quite frankly, would have come from out of state. That's where all the applications came from, that's where all the premed programs were, particularly the Northeast. Back then, we could have filled three classes of well-qualified students just from Pennsylvania if we had wanted to.*

Roland Sharp: Later the Board of Regents found out that they could trade some osteopathic openings with other states for openings in fields that West Virginia universities don't offer, such as veterinary medicine and architectural engineering. So the school now takes about three-fourths of its students from West Virginia and the rest from other states.

Fred Smith: *We decided not to stay private. We didn't want to change our mission, and we decided that once you double up tuition and get people in from wherever, they have a tendency to be more interested in what I call the high-tech or super-specialties. Then you lose your primary-care emphasis and you also lose that group of students who we think would make, maybe in many cases, the best physicians—those who are from rural Appalachia, rural West Virginia, who understand the need and who have better people skills, and who have a better understanding of the average person on the street.*

So we made that decision and we went to see Governor Arch Moore, to see if he would bring us into the state system. Well, he didn't hesitate, and he recommended to the Legislature a bill to bring us into the state higher education system under the Board of Regents.

The Governor Gets Involved

ROLAND SHARP: Governor Moore was 100 percent for the school. He was a friend of Dr. Wallington's to start with and the second thing was that Dr. Wallington sold him on it just like he sold us. Governor Moore said, "More power to you. Keep going! We'll make it a state institution if you can get accreditation."

Once, when we thought we weren't going to get accreditation, Governor Moore brought a bunch of us in and said, "What would happen if we went ahead and started this school and graduated students without approval?"

Our answer was, "They couldn't be licensed anywhere unless West Virginia passed a law that they could take the board exam in West Virginia."

He sat there thinking a little bit and he said, "Looks to me like that's a good idea. That's one of the ways we can be sure of getting doctors in West Virginia. If they couldn't take the board anywhere else, they would all have to stay here! Go talk to the Legislature."

We went to the Legislature and the Legislature said, "It's a good idea, but we can't afford it. We could support a school, but we can't support a hospital. WVU just grounded us. We can barely finance it."

My answer to them was, "We don't need a hospital. We can contract with hospitals." Members of the Legislature had never heard of that. I was pretty familiar with medical schools because when I taught at Kirksville we would attend AMA and AOA meetings yearly. I found out in those meetings that Harvard didn't own a hospital and neither did Emory University in Atlanta. Harvard used Massachusetts General and Peter Bent Brigham Hospital. Grady Hospital in Atlanta was Emory

Arch A. Moore, Governor of West Virginia 1969 - 1977 and 1985-1989. Governor Moore was a key supporter of the osteopathic medical school.

University's hospital. Cook County Hospital in Chicago was Chicago Medical School's only hospital.

Just as soon as the Legislature met, Governor Moore kept his word and spoke up, without even telling us ahead of time. In his speech, the state-of-the-state address that he gives them with all the things he was asking the Legislature to do, he said, "I am asking that you change the Greenbrier College of Osteopathic Medicine to the West Virginia School of Osteopathic Medicine [to make the name compatible with the WVU School of Medicine], immediately put it under the direction of the Board of Regents and finance the institution." At that time the Board of Regents was the administrative arm that ran all public higher education in West Virginia. Now there is a separate board of regents for the medical schools in the state.

We would get $500,000 to pay off our debt, but we would assign the title of the institution to the state. That was a great deal for the state! By that time, it was a ten or twenty million dollar plant, after you got all those laboratories put in.

As I said, Governor Moore gave a speech to the Legislature. He didn't even tell us. We heard it on TV that he requested that the Greenbrier College of Osteopathic Medicine be brought into the state system and renamed the West Virginia School of Osteopathic Medicine. The Legislature passed that, I think in the House something like eighty-seven to twelve. A big majority in the Senate passed it too, and they sent that on to the Board of Regents. The Board of Regents immediately announced that they were not going to accept it, because, one, they already had one school that they were having trouble financing and, two, the Legislature did not say when it would come under the control of the Board of Regents. The governor was furious. He called a special session of the Legislature and they voted immediately to locate the West Virginia School of Osteopathic Medicine [WVSOM] in Lewisburg and to provide a budget line item for the school for ten years. The bill passed November 5, 1975. The school was to become a ward of the Board of Regents by December 31, 1975. Then the chancellor of the Board of Regents,

Dr. Ben Morton, called me and said, "Could you be in Charleston by tomorrow morning?" I went to Charleston the next morning

The Chancellor said, "We didn't want your school. We got you. Now since we got you, I want you to go first class. Now you go back up to Lewisburg with your business manager and make a good budget and don't skimp on anything, because if I'm going to have an osteopathic school, I want it to be good."

So we went back there and made our budget and took it back to the Finance Committee of the Legislature, and they passed it right away. You know the budget for the medical school at WVU was about thirty or forty million and ours was only about three or four million.

The Board of Regents approved for us a $4,000,000 budget for that year. The legislature had made the school's budget a line item in the state budget for the next ten years. In other words if the Board of Regents were controlling us, they could say, "We'll give you a million and a half this year," when the legislature had given us four million. The Board of Regents doesn't have to spend four million unless it's a line item. Somebody in the Legislature said, "Let's make it a line item and that way, they have to spend it all on you. They cannot spend one nickel of that on any other state school. If you don't use it up, it just goes back in the state treasury." They kept us on a line item for six or seven years out of fear that *The Charleston Gazette* or some other influential group might try to do away with the institution. They might say, "Well, we've got enough doctors in West Virginia." If you had a Board of Regents that had a predominance of people who were against you, they could vote to recommend closing you.

Now, since the school has become so popular, there would probably be a toss-up about which medical school to close first; Lewisburg or the University or Marshall. This school has put more doctors in West Virginia than both Marshall and WVU. It wasn't any time until all the newspapers in the state except the *Gazette* were supporting us. Even the Huntington newspapers supported us. That's where the third medical school in West Virginia is now located, at Marshall University. I think the Huntington papers felt obligated since the members of the Legislature who supported us also supported Marshall.

Opal's Role

Opal was a big help in starting the school in Lewisburg. She was fantastic, because we had so much correspondence and so many articles in the newspaper. Most of them were against. We let her read all of them. And time and again, she always said, "Don't answer this one. This one you answer with a compliment." Newspaper reporters always ask questions that you could get another question and that will prompt another question. If you answer one that isn't favorable, you start a real dispute. So many times, when we got those and read them, and every time there was anything that we had to make a decision on, Fred Smith would say, "Let's ask Opal before we do this." She was the unofficial public relations director. Absolutely.

Facilities

In the meantime, while we were having all these problems with the accrediting body, we were applying for Hill-Burton funds and Appalachian Regional Commission funds. Sue Keller, Fred Smith, Dr. Bailes, Dr. Elizabeth Blatt, and I worked on that grant for Hill-Burton funds. By sometime early in 1973, we had that grant work completed. It was no trouble to get that through because our Congressman Harley Staggers, Senior, had been in Congress something like twelve terms. He could get anything he wanted. It wasn't any time until he informed us that we had those funds.

We got a $1,300,000 grant from Hill-Burton. We used the money to convert classrooms and laboratories formerly used by students at the Greenbrier Military Academy. The laboratories had to be updated, the classrooms had to be renovated, and offices had to be built for the faculty we had hired. Then we had to buy all the equipment for the laboratories. We needed a microbiology laboratory, a physiology laboratory, and a gross anatomy laboratory for dissection. All of that had to be bought, and that took a lot of money.

We hired contractors to renovate the physical plant. When we were a private school, an architectural firm came up from Roanoke and did all the stuff for almost nothing. They just liked the idea of what we were doing. They were another case of people saying, "Just pay us if you can." These new facilities are incredible. When we announced that we were going to start a school for general practitioners, people were really excited. Each school has to have an initial statement, a reason for its existence, and ours was to train GPs. People were very interested.

We renovated that whole big military school and converted the quadrangle into offices, ideal offices and laboratories for the faculty. Then the next thing that came was to build a new science building. [Frederic W. Smith Science Building - 1991] When it was opened, Dr. Weston, the chancellor of the three medical schools in West Virginia, said it was an anatomy science building of the first order—not even Harvard could approach the quality. At that time it was the most outstanding anatomy laboratory of its kind. They have stainless steel tables with vapor collectors for the cadavers used in dissection. The lab didn't even smell like a lab!

Where I worked in Morgantown in the laboratory in the late 1930s, you just cried all afternoon like you were peeling onions. The formaldehyde from the body that was preserved just came up in your eyes and you blew your nose and wiped your eyes as you worked. At the new school you could just sit there with none of that. When I went to school we worked on old wooden tables and formaldehyde would drip down on the floor from the bottom of the table. The new school has stainless steel tables that rolled that drip out. When the bodies are finished down here, they're cremated. We have a mausoleum in the cemetery

Roland Sharp Alumni Conference Center at WVSOM. The facility was dedicated August 24, 1995.
Photo courtesy of the West Virginia School of Osteopathic Medicine.

where anyone who wills their body to science and isn't claimed by kin gets a Christian burial. Their ashes rest in that mausoleum and we have one large enough to take care of donors for the next twenty five years.

Then they built the alumni conference center. That was built in 1995, mostly with contributions, and now they're going to double it in size. They named it for me, unjustly I think, because as I told you before, many people gave freely of their time, money, and moral support. Their contention was that I was the glue, or mortar, that held them all together, or they all would have gone home. When I accepted the honor, I did so in the name of all those who made that such a team. I've never known an institution with so many people who care so much. Why even Brad, the guy who clipped the grass, would be there early in the morning, and you'd have to run them all away in the evening!

Next Senator Byrd acquired the money to build the teaching clinic, [Robert C. Byrd Clinic – 1997] which is named after him. Next was a library. The medical library is the best of its kind in the state. They're connected up with medical libraries all over the country.

But I'm getting ahead of myself. In order to get supplies for students, we had a company come with a motorized laboratory that had everything set up in it that you could look at. They sold microscopes and they would sell them or rent them to our students. In the first four years they would come from Chicago or Detroit and park on campus about a week before the academic year started. A lot of other schools were trying to buy all those things or forcing the students to do it. We were able to get these various companies to come to us.

Everybody was helpful except the accrediting body, the Board of Regents, and *The Charleston Gazette!*

A Faculty, A Curriculum, A Class

1972–1978

"We didn't originate the idea, but we were the first to implement an integrated faculty and curriculum."
—Roland Sharp

As in the previous chapter, this one has been compiled from interviews with Roland Sharp in the fall of 2001 and from a talk Fred Smith gave to WVSOM students in March 1991. Dr. Sharp and Mr. Smith worked closely together to found WVSOM.

ROLAND SHARP: In the beginning the faculty consisted only of Sue Keller in microbiology, Dr. Elizabeth Blatt from Concord College in physiology, Fred Smith in administration, and me.

So we had some faculty employed, but we had to have a full faculty - two in each basic science department, two anatomists, two physiologists, two biochemists, two pathologists, and two microbiologists. You had to have at least two. The accrediting body gave us the go-ahead the 15th of October 1974.

Recruiting a Faculty

Now remember that the accrediting group had said, "The town is too little. You won't be able to get faculty." Well, all the faculty members who came to Lewisburg loved it and after we had two or three visit, they were telling friends of theirs from all over the country to apply.

Roland Sharp teaching anatomy to first year students, 1974. He helped teach a number of classes while recruiting to build up the faculty. Photo courtesy of the West Virginia School of Osteopathic Medicine.

I asked Dr. Blatt to employ another physiologist. I asked Sue to check on another microbiologist and I would check with the osteopathic medical school at Kirksville. We got Dr. Khan, a native of Pakistan who was teaching at the Kirksville school but who wasn't head of the department. He wanted to chair a department somewhere, so he came to West Virginia and stayed until the year I left the school, 1978. We got an anatomist from the University of Georgia and it wasn't but another year and we had two or three anatomists.

We got Dr. John Sharp as a biochemist. He grew up here in Pocahontas County, and he had a Ph.D. in biochemistry and was a research chemist with the Upjohn Company in Kalamazoo, Michigan. He didn't like living up there. I didn't know John then, even though we are related. John's father and I are first cousins. [John is also the great nephew of the late Drs. Jim Price and Norman Price of Pocahontas County] I really only knew John by sight, but I knew he had a Ph.D. and Fred Smith and John were good friends. He and Fred talked, and Fred said, "I'm gonna hire John Sharp. He wants to come back to West Virginia. He is doing research on prostaglandins for Upjohn." So he came back. Right after I left the school, Dr. John Sharp resigned from the faculty and applied to become a [medical] student here. Sue Keller also resigned to become a student.

We found another young fellow, Bob Peck, with a Ph.D., living down at Hinton on a farm. He's still there on the farm, I believe. Somebody told us that there was a group of what they called hippies that moved in around here in the sixties and some of them had doctorates. Folks said, "There is one who is doing research on medicinal plants and he goes to the University of New Hampshire once or twice a year to report on that. They may be supporting him." I contacted him, he was interested, and so I wrote to the University of Pennsylvania where he got his Ph.D. I wrote the chairman of the Department of Chemistry there and the letter that I got back from him stated that "In my ten years as chairman, Robert Peck was the most outstanding biochemistry student here." He also added that, "As a research biochemist, he is without peer," and this guy was farming!

Dr. Peck was not put on the three-year tenure track as was usual, though, because I thought we should wait a longer period to be sure of his commitment to the rigors of academic life. He was a great teacher. But if somebody had a Ph.D. and was as talented as that professor at the University of Pennsylvania said he was, and that somebody was living up on a mountain in a little homemade cabin and raising chickens, would you be concerned about his priorities? I also thought that he might want to go back to raising chickens when our next class came in. He commuted from the farm in Hinton all the time he was teaching, except in bad weather. I must admit that he was brilliant and one of the most colorful characters on our faculty. I could sit and talk to him all day long. I'd like to see him now and wish that he had stayed at the medical school.

There was another faculty member who had a science doctorate, Steve Richman, who is now on the staff of the Appalachian Regional Health Care Hospital in Hinton. He applied as a student at the school after he had taught with us for a couple of years and he's probably one of the most outstanding doctors in the Hinton area. He was chief of staff, emergency room doctor, and everything at the Hinton hospital! When they opened that hospital new, they didn't have anybody else and he really made it go. He and Dr. Peck came from the same area.

Most of the faculty were hired just before we become a state school. The founders put up some money and with $166,000 from the Appalachian Regional Commission, we had a little budget. We couldn't pay much, but we gave the faculty a token salary until we became a state school, which was November, 1975. The first class had just completed their first year. Then we could pay everybody the back salary. They took just what we could offer them and so did I. I got nothing extra for being President.

Right after November 1, 1975, everybody started getting their salary, which was line-item budgeted and controlled through the Board of Regents, as advised by the Chancellor. Ralph Williams was the state senator from the Greenbrier County area, and we need to give him plenty of credit for giving us that line item, so that we were guaranteed the money each year.

The chancellor, Dr. Morton, told me to make the budget and make it good, and I did. By the next year we had two pathologists, three in anatomy, three microbiologists and Dr. Blatt had hired two more physiologists. I no longer had to teach and could devote myself to administrative work. Dr. Blatt was acting preclinical dean for a while. The man she hired as the first physiologist became preclinical dean and helped us develop the integrated curriculum. He's the only person who is still there in the same position as he was when the school opened. His name is Mike Cope. He has a Ph.D. from Ohio State and he brought another Ph.D. from Ohio State who was of Russian descent. He was American-born, Bence Boelcskevy. It was said that he was a descendant of the royal family in Russia. We had some really outstanding people there.

We hired a man and his wife, the Higginbothams, anatomists who were retiring from WVU. As a matter of fact, they didn't really want to retire, but WVU retired them because they had reached age sixty five. Frances and Curtis Higginbotham had been at three medical schools and at West Virginia for the last fifteen years. At sixty five they came to our school and they stayed there until after we graduated three or four classes.

In addition to physiology, I also taught histology to the first two classes—that's microscopic anatomy. I taught Pathology I to the first and second class. That's the first half of pathology. That's what I was teaching when I left Kirksville, but then my wife insisted that I not teach it anymore. Opal said, "You're too far behind!" And I said, "Any old slide of the skin that I have in my microscope looks just the same as if it were taken from somebody's skin today." There was no change in microbiology. There were still the same blood vessels, the same muscles, the same nerves, etcetera. But she thought that my teaching subjects would be like my medical practice. If someone had been trying to teach practice courses, and had been out of school a long time, if someone was trying to teach urology and hadn't been in school for fifteen years, then they wouldn't be up to date. They would be reasonably up to date, but they certainly wouldn't be on par with someone graduating right then.

Building the Nation's First Integrated Curriculum

We decided at WVSOM that we would have an integrated program—that we would not have a program where you take course after course after course and then try to put it all together in two years, the way most medical schools did. We wanted to start a school in which the faculty was integrated, where everyone knew what the other was teaching. When the student finishes studying the anatomy of the kidney, he will know the diseases, the physiology, and the chemistry of the kidney, just as though he were a senior. It was going to be that integrated.

Dr. Curtis Higginbotham told me, "I was at Northwestern. I was in Florida. I was at the Medical College of South Carolina, and WVU, and this is the only time that I ever knew what I was really doing." He said, "The only time I ever knew the physiologist or the biochemist at those colleges is when we were introduced at a social affair." He said, "These are the best years of my life. We are really teaching doctors. Working so closely with the other doctors, I have learned more here than I learned in all those other years because I know the physiology of the organ I'm teaching, the pathology, the microbiology, all that." He and his wife liked it so well. They liked that way of teaching.

Oh, the faculty was a very close-knit group. We had meetings two or three times a week where the biochemists told the rest of the faculty what they were teaching that week, the microbiologists told what they were teaching each week, the gross anatomists did the same. Everybody on our faculty knew what the other faculty members were teaching. That's where our curriculum was totally different from other medical schools, because everybody was teaching in the same category.

When I was in medical school at Morgantown, you would take anatomy, but the biochemist didn't know anything at all about what you were studying in anatomy. When we [at WVSOM] taught about the hand, the physiologist taught the function and the movement of the hand, the use of it, and about the fingers. Then the microbiologist taught all about the bacteria that would usually infect your skin. So when a student finished one part of the body like the hand, he knew the anatomy of the hand, the physiology, the microbiology, the diseases that would affect it, and the pathology—all of the organic problems that you could have with that body part. A freshman student would learn that in one semester.

Our novel curriculum was really not like that at any other medical school. Really, ours was more modern. The students at WVSOM were learning about, discussing, and seeing patients in the second semester of their first year.

What our medical school and the newer faculty wanted to do was put clinical training earlier. Let medical students see some patients in their first year and second year. When I went to medical school, you didn't even have the opportunity to say hello to a patient. Students were clearly isolated. There weren't even any patients at Morgantown. You had to go to Richmond for the last two years. All you saw was basic science people and you heard nothing about disease.

When our students went to a hospital in their third year, the hospital staff would tell us, "These kids know as much as our fourth year students that we're getting from the other schools. How are you doing it?" The integrated curriculum made us very popular. Every hospital wanted more and more students from Lewisburg.

You can understand now, can't you, what I'm talking about? Integrating the curriculum? There was no such thing as just a course curriculum. It was a totally integrated curriculum.

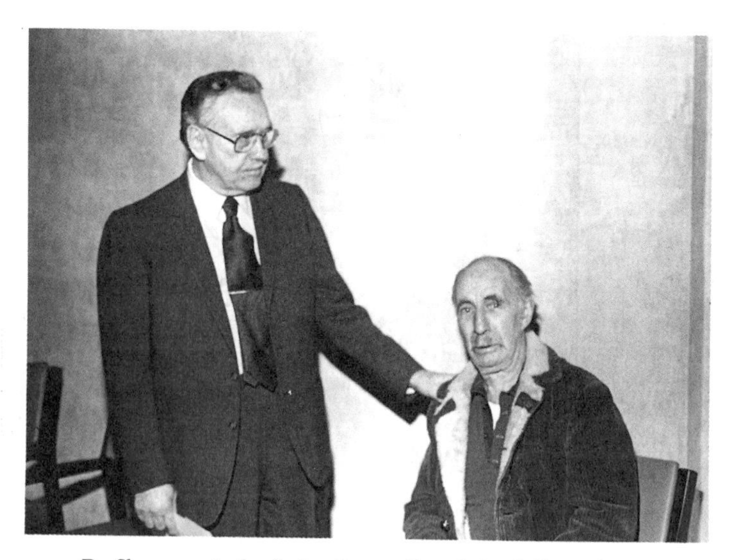

Dr. Sharp greets the first patient at Greenbrier College of Osteopathic Medicine Clinic - circa 1974. Photo Courtesy of the West Virginia School of Osteopathic Medicine.

Dr. Joe Rogers from Michigan was a prominent cardiologist and his wife Sheila was a specialist in electrocardiography. We hired him as a temporary academic dean and the two of them concentrated on planning the curriculum. Unfortunately, his administrative tenure didn't work out. He was a very intelligent man, but he was also - let's put it this way - pretty unschooled in politics and tact. He told off the accreditation group when they came in.

He said, "That's a better curriculum than you can make and I won't change it."They [the accreditation committee] told me as the president, "If you don't change it, you're not going to get any further."I asked Dr. Rogers, "Change it and when they leave, when they're out of here, we'll do it any way we want to do it."

"No way," he said, "I don't compromise my convictions. You and I have considered this. We went up to New York to Stony Brook to the new medical school up there. We spent two days consulting with them on curriculum. We consulted with Dr. Wilbur Cole from Kansas City, the dean who came to help us with applicants. We went to four or five medical schools and talked with their deans."

The curriculum that Dr. Rogers and I came up with was better than what the accrediting body had. But they said, "If you don't follow our plan, you don't get any further with your accreditation; either that, or you need to reconsider your dean."

So I had to tell Dr. Rogers, "You're no longer dean. Dr. Jerry Bailes will be acting dean for the next six months." I sent Dr. Bailes in to talk with the accrediting body, and he accepted their recommendations.

Dr. Archie Feinstein, from Philadelphia College of Osteopathic Medicine, was on that accrediting committee and he said, "When the committee breaks up, I'll come back from Philadelphia and work with you. I think your curriculum is the best. I had to agree with the committee to get you accreditation, but I will come back, if you would like me to work with you." He came back in two or three weeks, stayed for a week, working with me to fine-tune the curriculum and didn't charge us anything for his visit.

Dr. Rogers went back to Michigan to practice and Dr. Bailes stayed the academic dean for six months or so until we were able to replace him. The first permanent academic dean was Dr. Harry Kornhiser, a neurologist who served well. When another president came in, the second one after me, he evidently didn't like Dr. Kornhiser very well. After a year or two he advised Dr. Kornhiser that he was getting another dean. So Dr. Kornhiser left and took a residency in psychiatry at the University of Michigan. Then he came back to the area and became the chairman of neuropsychiatry at Allegheny Regional Hospital at Low Moor, Virginia. He's been there ever since.

I would never have known about the possibility of integrating the curriculum if I hadn't regularly attended the annual meetings of the American Medical Association's Congress of Medical Education. What the AMA had been trying to do for some years was to get their medical schools to teach the students something about disease when they were teaching the basic sciences. The consensus was that the entire teaching force at the schools would have to turn over before that would happen.

For instance, when you're teaching chemistry and when you're teaching carbohydrates, you should also teach a great deal about diabetes. If you're teaching fats in biochemistry, you should teach students right then about cholesterols and the diseases and problems that cholesterols can cause. Before that time, in all the medical schools in the country, you never heard about those types of things until you got in what was called a practice course. Anatomy, physiology, biochemistry, bacteriology, pathology and pharmacology are your basic sciences. When anatomy was taught, we wanted the anatomist to teach about muscular diseases and diseases of the joints and show them in anatomy. That's a freshman course.

We didn't originate the idea, but we were the first to implement an integrated faculty and curriculum.

We started with one of the most modern programs in the country. At the end of the third year, when we had become a state school, they couldn't do much but give us full accreditation. We were totally financed, we had the physical facility, and we had the students. So we got full accreditation. Then we just put in place the full curriculum that we wanted. That's why Dr. Michael Cope is still the preclinical dean, because he was one of the few people at that time who was familiar with this kind of curriculum. Then he was only about twenty-five years old. Other medical schools really wanted to adopt a curriculum like ours but they couldn't get the older members of their faculty to go along with it.

Finding Hospitals and Clinics for Rotations

Well, we didn't have a hospital for our clinical rotations. My idea was to take a little time and go to various hospitals and see how many would agree to let us train students in their hospital. It wasn't but three or four months until we had twenty or thirty hospitals that had volunteered. We had enough right in the area! Allegheny Regional Hospital was just finishing up [construction] and it had as many beds as the hospital at WVU. We got the state hospital in Welch, Logan General Hospital, and that was all we needed at the time.

Sun Coast Hospital, an osteopathic hospital in Clearwater, Florida, was bigger than the WVU hospital, and they offered to take all of our students. It was accredited for training and they would just as soon take all their students from one institution as to take three or four from twelve different places. We were only admitting thirty six students. Our first-year class went to Sun Coast for everything because they were so well set up for a variety of rotations. It was a teaching institution. Now, over the last ten years or so, none of our students has gone to Florida. But that hospital is the one that really started us.

Allegheny Regional had plenty of beds, but it didn't have the organization. They would take a couple of students at a time, but it would take them a couple of years to really get organized so that they could take a lot of students. Allegheny Regional, Logan, Charleston Area Medical Center, the Beckley hospitals, the Bluefield hospitals, Clarksburg, and Princeton—while all of them are signed up for students, there are so few students that not many of the institutions get more than two or three students. And I think that the quality of training that our students got from the very beginning was just as good as the training one could get in Morgantown or at any big university.

We didn't use just hospitals for training sites. We also used clinics. After I came back to practice at Green Bank, the school could send students up to me. I could take one student for a month, but I have taken students ever since I came out of medical school myself. I took them from Kirksville, from Philadelphia, from Ohio, and from Chicago. I've had students at Green Bank from all over the country. I have taken students who wanted to be trained in rural medicine or industrial medicine from the time I first began [right after World War II].

Grounding the Students in History

FRED SMITH: *We were able to fight those battles and secure pre-accreditation status, which is all you can get to start a school. Then they come in a couple of years after you start and, if everything goes well, I think they come in after five years and you get full accreditation.*

We started our first class in 1974 as the Greenbrier College of Osteopathic Medicine, a private school. We renovated the facilities as much as we could. It was very minimal, and we started with thirty six students and about seven faculty members. I guess all told, if you counted secretaries, maintenance, housekeeping administration, and faculty, we didn't have more than seventeen people total at the beginning. Of course, we used a lot of visiting lecturers and many of our state society members would come in and lecture. Dr. Sharp lectured full time. I taught the history of osteopathic medicine. I was a history major in undergraduate school.

We all wore a lot of hats. I know this sounds ridiculous to you, even knowing what my background was, in educational administration, but I was chair of the curriculum committee. I helped work up the curriculum. I did the formatting for it and Dr. Sharp and some of us went to [the State University of New York at] Stony Brook and WVU, but to Stony Brook in particular because they were approaching having an integrated curriculum. We looked at the format of the systems approach to see how that worked and if that's what we wanted to use. That's what we started with here. There's been a lot of arranging and adjustments, but we still use the systems approach with our curriculum. It's been very successful and we've built a good national reputation with that over the years.

This is really weird today, but when I was up in Washington, D.C., at an American Osteopathic Association meeting, I heard a Dr. Ward from Illinois give a lecture. I don't remember the exact topic, but it was geared for non-physicians as well as physicians and it was a topic on osteopathic medicine, with a lot of emphasis on manipulation and the osteopathic philosophy and all that. I thought, "Boy, how appropriate. Did they bring this guy here just for this purpose?" I went to that session because that was one of the topics at the national convention that I felt like I could probably understand. I left that meeting and rushed to Dr. Sharp, and I said, "Dr. Sharp, I just heard a presentation. We have to get this guy to our campus, to talk to our preclinical faculty and to our students and our staff because we all need an orientation on osteopathic medicine. You know, what is the profession? What is manipulation? What is the philosophy?" We called Dr. Ward, and he agreed to come down every fall. That was fantastic and that was what we needed.

The First Classes

ROLAND SHARP: We had a place to have the school, we had remodeled, we had accreditation, we had grant money to start on, we had faculty, and all we needed were students. How did we get them? We had 400 applicants before we were ever accredited. So they gave us temporary accreditation. We had applicants galore, 400 or 500 applications that we had to go over. We needed help. Dr. Wilbur Cole, Dean of the Kansas City College of Osteopathic Medicine, came. He was a classmate of mine at Kirksville. He came to Lewisburg free. We had so much free help that I felt embarrassed. Everyone we asked helped. Dr. Cole reviewed all of the applications. He put one pile here, "These are highly desirable. This group is acceptable. This group, don't consider." He had been dean of that school for twenty-some years and he really knew what it took to be a medical student.

We picked out a class of thirty six. They were all West Virginians but one, who was from Marietta, Ohio. The accrediting body said, "You can only take thirty six because your laboratories will only accommodate thirty six students and you have the faculty requirement for thirty six, so we'll temporarily let you go ahead." I was sitting in one of the visiting rooms in one of the big hotels in Kansas City, and I heard one [of the committee members] say, "Well, we'll give it to them, but I'll bet you two to one that it goes down the drain." Anyway, we were happy and came back and started our first class.

Whenever it was mentioned in the newspapers that we were having a school in Lewisburg, we had people write us requesting applications. Last year [2001] for the sixty-eight or seventy spaces—that's all they could take—there were 1,408 applications. There are far more applicants for medical school than there are spaces. I have told students all my life, "It is a privilege to be a doctor, not a right, because many people were turned down so that you could have your place." I never hesitate to tell students, or doctors, that. At Lewisburg, we often get more applications per opening than either Marshall or WVU medical schools.

In the first class of students fifty percent had master's degrees. They were older, most of them were married, and there were more children than there were students. Some had two or three children. They had applied to medical schools in the past and were just waiting in graduate school to reapply. Half of them came from WVU. They'd been turned down a couple of times and they were just looking to get to medical school before they felt like they were too old. They were a smart bunch of kids. They just weren't accepted at WVU because WVU could accept only so many. They were the three or the four applicants who were left out when someone else was accepted into an opening up there.

I don't know any of them, not a single one, who isn't happy or pleased that they came to Lewisburg. And practically all of them I've talked to have said, "We knew more than the graduates in Morgantown by far. When we went to hospitals where we would have a senior from Morgantown, he always wanted to know, 'Where'd you learn that? How'd you know that?'" So you know how that made our students feel. They felt a little bit superior!

The students and the faculty were just like one group. They came together as students, as advisors, as faculty members, as friends. Until we had four classes of students, it was just like a family. In all of the social affairs, students were integrated right in with the faculty. It was like that until the school got a good-sized faculty and four years of students. Then there were student representatives and faculty representatives for social and governing purposes. There were so many that they couldn't all be at an affair. But for the first two classes, everyone knew what everyone else knew. That's the way it was.

We met our objective. The objective was to train family physicians for patients in rural areas, especially Appalachia. That could be anywhere from Birmingham, Alabama, all the way up to northern New York.

My best memories of my time at the school come from interacting with the students and teaching them to help integrate the classroom materials with the clinical training. You see, basic science people are Ph.D.s, so you had to have a few doctors to help them put their basic sciences into a clinical training program. It was a real challenge, but I would say that our basic science Ph.D.s would have been pretty good doctors after those first four years, just from having to integrate their subjects into the clinical program. I'd say about any of our Ph.D.s would have made good GPs, because the doctors had talked with them so much about the various phases that they were teaching, in talking about the diseases that are associated with their science coursework. All the basic science people sat in and listened to this instruction, you see. When the doctor was telling the physiologist about the physiology of certain diseases, the anatomist was hearing that too—they were all hearing it. I think that's why Dr. John Sharp resigned his faculty position. I think he thought, "Well, I can be a doctor and won't have to study much. I've listened to all this! All I'll have to do is get hospital training now."

Eventually, we doubled our faculty, doubled our classroom space, and enlarged our laboratories. Then the accrediting body gave us permission to accept more students. The school can take sixty-six now. They'll go up to seventy-two next year. [In 2007–08 the West Virginia School of Osteopathic Medicine had 211 students in the first year class.]

The Early Days

FRED SMITH: *We've increased our class size. We've fought those battles. We've had a lot of changes in our facilities here. When we first started, the facilities were military school facilities. When we purchased this place, we purchased it lock, stock, and barrel. We had the band uniforms, the library books, the cafeteria equipment, the barber shop, the laundry. Our first convocation, we were sitting on the stage during a downpour of rain and the plaster on the ceiling was falling off near the sides onto the floor. People started moving into the center. We were sitting up there and just praying that the roof didn't cave in, but we didn't stop. We kept on going!*

ROLAND SHARP: Jack Bailey, who came to the school right after it was purchased, was employed by Dr. Frank Wallington for the corporation. He'd been city manager in a town near Dr.

Wallington. Jack had been an assistant to West Virginia Governor, Hulett Smith, who had recently completed his term. Mr. Bailey looked after the whole facility. He sold the equipment piece by piece, and he basically kept the plant dry and warm during the first two winters before the school opened.

Jack was also well known in state and congressional political circles. He was not only of great physical assistance but also of major political assistance. He was totally sold on the project.

FRED SMITH: *There was a specific provision in the legal documents of the Greenbrier Military School that attorneys told us they had never seen before. It was unique, that they could not sell the property here for any more than the value that was placed on the stock that was in that corporation, and that value was $350,000. That's what we purchased this place for. Forty acres, all these homes, everything on this block, and a couple of houses down the street. We still have all the property we bought. I can tell you, the local realtors around here were going crazy. They were over here talking to us and everything. They wanted to try to get some of this property.*

It's been a fascinating experience for me personally. It's been a great experience and I'm, as you can tell, as a non-physician, a true believer in osteopathic medicine. What it stands for. What it does.

When we first started, we had a serious problem with housing for students. We had to house students where the cadets used to sleep, over where the clinic is now, and in apartments where faculty for the military school stayed. Our faculty stayed with their families. Dr. Sharp and I had an apartment where the clinical training office is now. That was a faculty apartment. We both lived in Pocahontas County, and we'd both come down and stay in the apartment. People would come through the apartment at all hours of the night. Faculty and students would be sitting there talking. It was a great experience.

ROLAND SHARP: It was complicated and it was a long siege, but according to *US News & World Report,* the year before last, it was one of the better medical schools. Recently WVSOM was ranked in the top fifty of the 145 medical schools and it ranked number one in family practice. It was number three the year before. Neither Marshall University nor WVU was even mentioned in the top fifty. That's no reflection on them. It's just a reflection on this institution and the fact that we were able to get a facility and enough good faculty to put all of this into action.

The school's really a nice place. If you look at some of the statistics they put out, like how many jobs it added to the area and how many millions of dollars it put in the local economy, it has really been good. And it still receives only about $6,000,000 in appropriations. Compared to the other schools, that's nothing. Mostly it's because WVSOM doesn't have to support a hospital of any sort. They just have to keep up the school. And I would never have known that you didn't need a hospital if I hadn't been attending all those congresses of the American Medical Association year after year.

Our philosophy in starting was to prepare family physicians for West Virginia and Appalachia. That was the statement of purpose that we put in the charter for the Greenbrier College of Osteopathic Medicine. That was the statement of purpose that we gave the Appalachian Regional Commission and Hill-Burton. It's still their statement of purpose—to prepare physicians to practice in the rural areas of West Virginia and Appalachia. That's why preference is given to West Virginia applicants.

More of the graduates have stayed in West Virginia from our school than from both Marshall and WVU. WVU took twice the number of students and Marshall is taking more now. But the school at Lewisburg concentrates more on family practice and tries to indoctrinate the students in family practice instead of a specialization. If you specialize, they prefer that you specialize in family medicine. At least four hundred of them have gone to rural areas of West Virginia, and that's a lot of doctors in twenty-some years.

Dr. Sharp, shown here "white-coating" Heidi Hartman in 2003, is still interacting with students. Photo courtesy of the West Virginia School of Osteopathic Medicine.

A New Partner

1978- Present

"She was a very attractive lady."
-Roland Sharp

During the mid-1970s my life was changing dramatically. I was working with colleagues, lawmakers, and friends to open a school of osteopathic medicine at Lewisburg. My first wife passed away in early 1978 from cancer. At that time and for a while after that, I concluded that, at my age, I would never marry again. Opal and I had been married for over forty-six years.

At that time I was on the state Health Systems Agency Board, representing the osteopathic profession. My present wife, Kit, had become a member of the board, representing the public from the area of Ansted. I was attending a medical convention in Huntington, West Virginia, and there was a meeting of the Health Systems Agency in Charleston. I was to stop and participate in that on the way back. However, I was somewhat depressed and I wasted a lot of time on the way. I didn't get to the meeting until rather late in the evening. As the meeting broke up, several people I knew came over and spoke to me. My present wife, Thelma "Kit" Neal, was with the group. They introduced her.

A few minutes later she came over and said, "I'm Charles Lee Neal's mother." Well, he was a student in the new osteopathic school at Lewisburg. I remembered him well because his father had been killed in a tractor accident on the farm while Lee was in school. His father was a school man, an assistant superintendent of schools in Fayette County, but [he] also lived on and operated a farm. Fred Smith, one of my associates at the School of Osteopathic Medicine, came to me after the man was killed and said that this young man was going to leave school and go back to the farm. Fred asked me to call the young man and persuade him to stay. I called him in and talked with him for some time, a half-hour or more, and urged him to stay in school. He could do a lot more for his mom and sister if he stayed in school than he could ever do on the farm. Of course when Kit said, "I'm Charles Lee Neal's mother," I became more interested. In our conversation, I asked if she had any other children. She said that she had one daughter, who was a freshman nursing student at WVU.

Well, I had made up my mind a long time before that that the main problem plaguing married couples was dealing with family and in-law issues. I began to think a little. She was a very attractive lady. I began to think, well if she has a son who's a doctor whom I know and a daughter who's a nurse, I can't imagine that my grandchildren would object. My son's children, four daughters and a son, were living in Delaware at the time.

Kit and I talked a considerable amount of time at the meetings. She invited me to stop at her farm in Ansted on my way back to Lewisburg. I stopped in and took a look at the farm, and I liked the place and, as I said, she was an attractive lady. I made the comment to her, "I might be interested in a lady like you if you weren't so young."

Very quickly she said, "I'm not so young. I'm already 55." So that's what started it up. I went back to Lewisburg and soon invited her to visit there. Today, I look back and chuckle about my first visit to her farm. She invited me in to see the farm and meet her daughter, but she didn't even offer me a Coca-Cola or a cup of coffee and she is a very fine hostess.

I spent several hours looking around. I've kidded her about that ever since. I must have been very unimpressive or she must have been very excited. I didn't know which. I suspected it was because I was unimpressive. But she accepted my invitation anyway and visited me up here at Frost.

Kit and Roland Sharp - picture taken in the 1980s.

Opal and I had a home near Athens that we had built for our retirement. The house was on her original home-place in Speedway. Kit came to see me over there while my granddaughters were visiting. They liked her very much. My mother was still living and Kit and my mother hit it off very well right from the start.

There was a national convention in Orlando, Florida, at Disney World that summer, and I was supposed to appear there to receive a special award from the Student Osteopathic Medical Association. They insisted that I come to the award ceremony. I asked Kit to go along with me if her daughter and one of my granddaughters could come along. It was all agreed, but about a week before we were to go, her daughter said that she had something else to do, a boyfriend or something. And about two days before, my granddaughter said, "Something's come up. I have to go back to Morgantown."

So Kit decided that she could not go with me to the meeting. She said, "People are doing things like that, but I don't think that would be a good example for my children and your grandchildren, so I won't be going." The next day I called her. Well, anyway, to get married then in West Virginia, you had to have a blood test, which took several days, and then you had to wait three days after getting your license before the ceremony could take place. A day or two before my time to go down there to Florida I had a bright idea.

My mother kept telling me, "Somebody else is going to get that woman, as good as she is and as good as she looks. Someone else is going to get her and you're going to be sitting there by yourself." So I called Kit and said we could get married tomorrow in Monterey, Virginia. I explained a colleague over there could arrange the blood tests. Moreover, Virginia did not have the waiting period.

She hesitated a little while, but she said, "Okay I'll come," and she called her son for his blessing. He said, "Well, if you want to, don't wait for the family or anything, just go ahead."

After all, he knew me from his student days at the medical school in Lewisburg.

So she came to Frost and we went over to Monterey. We saw Dr. Billingsley at his house, and he arranged a blood test and helped us arrange to get the license at the Highland County Courthouse. I knew some of the good folks over there and they were all interested in helping us. They wondered whether we wanted to get married in a church or outside or somewhere else. "What church do you want?"

I said, "Presbyterian." Dr. Billingsley said, "It's right beside the courthouse here." Kit piped up and said, "Well, I'm a Methodist." He said, "That's down where the stoplight is. That's my church, and I can call the minister." I said, "It doesn't matter to me, whichever you want." She said, "I'd prefer the Methodist."

This gentleman called the Methodist minister, and he wanted to know if we wanted to come to the house or to the church. Kit thought we ought to go to the church, so we went there. We arrived before he did, and when he came to the church and looked at us, he was just stunned, and totally tactless. "I thought you two were young people!"

We all had a good laugh. He was only about in his thirties. He opened the door, took us in, and went through the ceremony. He had a huge pile of papers with him. Then when he got through the ceremony, he referred to the literature and talked to us a little bit about what the marriage bond truly means. But then he stopped suddenly and said, "You all are not interested in the rest. All of the rest of this material I have here is for young couples. It relates to birth control, so I am just going to let you go."

We left Monterey, came back across Route 250, and had our first supper at the Hermitage in Bartow, WV. That was January 16, 1979. Madge Bledsoe—the Bledsoes owned that inn—was the first one we told that we had gotten married and we had a good dinner there. Madge, by the way, is a cousin of mine. Madge's mother or grandmother was a Sharp. Every couple of years we go back to the Hermitage for our anniversary dinner. We did make it to the convention in Florida and we were married when we got there. I suppose that's the highlight of our story together, but it's been a very, very delightful, successful marriage. Her children are the same age as my grandchildren, and they all really like each other. My grandchildren and great-grandchildren call her Granny Kit. Kit's children, Lee and Holly, have taken to me just like I was their dad. In fact, I have been Holly's stepfather longer than her natural father, who died prematurely, was her dad. She reminded me of that about two birthdays ago. "You have been my dad longer than my real dad was."

A New Generation

When my grandparents needed help, or my grandfather or grandmother would be sick, my mother or my father said, "You go over and help grandpa today. You go over and help him work his garden." My wife asks her daughter if her grandson can come and dig up her flower bed, and her daughter says, "I will ask him and see if he can."

Now I make a comparison there of three generations. My parents said, "Your grandparents need you," and I knew, almost instinctively, that I should go. It was instilled in me that if they needed me, they didn't have to tell me, "I'm going to make you." They didn't ask me, "Do you want to go help your granddad hoe his garden today or help grandma dig up her flower beds?" They said, "Today, you go help grandma dig up the flower beds. She's not well." And to me, "not well" meant that Grandma had something wrong with her and Grandma might die or something. That's a big difference between generations.

As a result, my wife did not get her flower beds. Her back hurts and she's getting too old to dig up big flower beds like the ones she has at her house. She told me on the telephone today

Dr. Sharp and his wife Kit were the most popular people at the July, 2006, Maben Reunion, more than forty years after he'd moved back to Pocahontas County. Many of the babies he had delivered as a coal company doctor were there. Photo courtesy of Jack Feller.

that she has a man who's going to weed her flower bed and take care of it. She dug up most of it herself. Her daughter is a director of nursing at a big nursing home, and now she would have come over there and dug the flowerbed up for her mother if she could have got off in time. She would have done it, even if it had taken her until the middle of the night. However, she would "ask" her son if he wanted to, if he had time to, and he's a Junior in high school. He has a girlfriend, and he had a date or something, so he chose not to come.

I think that's the attitude that parents these days take with their children. "Do you want to go to school today?" My brother had four sons, and all of them graduated from high school. My brother told me twenty years ago, "My sons never would have gotten out of high school if it had depended on their mother." He said, "Really, I don't think my sons would have even gotten out of preschool [unless] I called them in the morning and said, 'Get up and go to school.' She would call them and say, 'Do you want to go to school this morning? It's seven o'clock.'" And he said if at seven they were still in bed, she never would have said, "You're supposed to go to school."

He said, "I said to my boys, 'When you get through with high school, you're going to college. I don't care what you take.' But she would have said, 'You just do what you please. If you want to go to college, OK. If you want to just stay here in the house with us, that's fine.' " Isn't that interesting? How does that attitude come about? And I don't say that the younger generation is wrong for their attitude.

Old people tell me, "You side with the young." My grandchildren love to come here because they can tell me all their problems and I don't criticize them. I just tell them, "OK. If that's the way you think, fine." I think that they all love me, and if I called them and said, "I'm sick," I think all five of them would be here before daylight.

EPILOG

Paths Taken and Not Taken

"I never took the path I had planned. Each time I was detoured, but the detour was always better."

"Go out and have some fun. I'm having fun. When people ask what I am doing for vacation, I tell them I am going to my office. That's fun."

—Roland Sharp

There have been amazing advances in science and medicine during my lifetime. We can diagnose almost anything, but, believe it or not, we have made very little progress in the treatment of cancer. Even the highest of medical associates realize that we are little beyond where we were fifty years ago. A few malignancies are treated successfully. There is palliative treatment, but as far as a cure is concerned, we're little beyond what we knew fifty years ago. You know that on observation. The reason our statistics look so much better is that we can recognize cancer early and surgically remove the malignancy. That's what puts our statistics up, not treatment. Stage Three malignancies still have the same rate of cure as they did decades ago. Someday I think we'll find a cure for cancer.

I really believe our Creator made something in nature to take care of any affliction that the human body can acquire. We just haven't found it. I think it's there if you believe that we were created. I don't believe that the Creator would generate life and then not put in place remedies for such afflictions and problems. I'm not referring just to health when I speak of creation. I'm referring to seasons, referring to climates, referring to planets. If there is a Creator, there is a plan. That's my attitude. There is no creation without a Creator and there can be no creation without a plan.

I think of everything in my life. I've had some adversity, but most everything in my life has evolved for something better. That's why I feel that I should keep paying back as long as I have the mental faculty to do so. God has certainly kept me alive and mentally here, I think, for something. Even starting late, I've still practiced longer than most doctors, over fifty years. Most of them just want to go into practice and retire as soon as they have enough years in to have a decent retirement income. They evidently do not like what they are doing.

Got a Headache? Do What You Love

I've been a doctor for fifty four years. I am ninety four years old, and I still have an active practice. [Dr. Sharp retired shortly after this interview.] Yes. Maybe I shouldn't, because many people, I guess, consider me too old, and I'm going to quit as soon as I'm physically too tired to work. That's something, but the number-one thing, really, is when I don't remember. I told Barbara [Barbara McCarty, Dr. Sharp's longtime nurse], "If a patient comes in and I don't remember the patient or I don't remember what they had before, you tell me and I'll go home."

I've always said you work as long as you can. If you want to live a life where you're contented and satisfied, socially and mentally at ease with yourself, you have to be at an occupation you love. People who are happy, optimistic, and free of headaches, nervous spells, insomnia—those are people who love what they're doing. I haven't slept poorly since I got out of medical school. I'm so involved in what I'm doing that if I have a problem outside my profession, I don't have time to worry about it.

If somebody chewed me out, it might have helped him sleep well to get it off his chest, but I'm going to be too busy to think about it.

Dr. Sharp in his garden.

That's my attitude about life. Just strive every day to work at things you like—what you can spend all your spare time thinking about. That's also why I ask my patients so much about themselves. If a patient comes in depressed or nervous, and I learn she loves to sing, I'm going to tell her, "Sing more!"

I still get the medical journals. I always look at the headlines. I still have that interest.

On Being a Good Doctor

We were taught that it was a privilege to be a doctor, not a right, because if it were a right, everyone who applied would come to medical school. It was a privilege and you had responsibility. With every privilege there is responsibility. They told you what your responsibilities were - to take care of sick people. There's a statement. It's not original.

As a doctor, you cure few or none, but you relieve many. You comfort all. That's not original, but I heard that quoted over and over by more than one of my instructors. I firmly believe I can't look back over my life and see people I cured. That's silly. If they get better, it's their own natural immunity. All you did was comfort them, support them, and their own natural immunity cured them. Do I sound like a doctor, or a preacher, or an idiot?

A Final Thought

I sometimes think God directs your life. There are so many paths to take in life. Somehow, when I came to a fork, I always seemed to take the one that got me where I needed to go. I never took the path I had planned. Each time I was detoured, but the detour was always better.

Some Thoughts About Medicine

Medicine Improves

"If there was a good doctor in your community and you wanted to be a doctor, you bought your bag and you went and lived with him for the next couple of years. You went on calls with him, helped him deliver babies, and watched what he did in surgery."

"Don't talk down to your patients. You're talking to a human spirit just like yourself. Treat them the same way you would want to be treated, and always consider that natural immunity is what gets you well, not the pill you take."

—Roland Sharp

My grandfather [George Jordan] was a doctor, but I don't think that was what made me want to be one. My grandfather was a native of Virginia who came to Pocahontas County from Pendleton County, West Virginia in 1900. It was nice to know that he had been a doctor and I read some of his magazines when I was in high school. But he never encouraged me to pursue a career in medicine. Back in his day doctors didn't make as much as school teachers. He would see countless patients each day, back in the teens and twenties. He'd ask for fifty cents, twenty five cents, and they'd say, "Charge it," so there was not a lot of financial incentive to become a physician.

What my grandfather did say was, "Choose a profession you like and educate yourself in that or you'll be working for someone else, for nothing, all your life."

Despite the financial disadvantages, the general consensus was that being a doctor was doing something that was good. Most of what I remember of him was delivering babies and pulling people's teeth.

Doctors and Drugs, Circa 1900

There were no real medicines back then. There were no antibiotics or cures, so many people had the attitude that going to the doctor was useless. There were no treatments for measles, for chicken pox, or whooping cough. They called the doctor only when children were dying. His visit was more for comfort and empathy than anything else because he had nothing to give the poor children.

Although medical training had changed radically by the 1930s, doctors still didn't have very many medicines they could use to treat disease. There were pain medications and antiseptics to clean wounds. Back in the 1850s and 1860s Ignaz Semmelweis in Vienna was the first person who claimed that bacteria caused disease and he tried to teach doctors that. I think medical history has it that he probably lost his mind or became a mental patient because nobody believed him. He spoke before doctors and they razzed him when he said that you should wash your hands before every surgery and before every delivery in obstetrics. They were doing surgery without antiseptics back then. Besides, they didn't wash their hands. They took care of the wounds on one patient and went over and dressed the wounds on the next patient. Maybe they washed their hands at the end of the day if they got them dirty. That's why so many died during the Civil War. If you were wounded, you would have been better off to just be killed because you were likely to die from infection anyway.

By 1900 the use of antiseptic became widespread. Bichloride of mercury was the first one and then phenol [carbolic acid], and iodine. I noticed then that when a doctor came to your house, they threw one of those tablets in a wash pan of water. It turned the water blue and they washed their hands with that blue solution. They were scrubbing before surgery and scrubbing the patient's wounds with antiseptic by then, but that was only required in major hospitals or big clinics.

Anesthetics came into existence about 1845. A dentist discovered ether, but ether wasn't too commonly used until after the Civil War. They could use that for an amputation, but most amputations were done by doctors who just gave the patient so much alcohol that he couldn't resist the surgery. As medical history goes, it would have been far better to have been killed in the Civil War than to have suffered under the treatment for wounds.

Until World War I, there were only two curative drugs—arsenic for syphilis and quinine for malaria—and you didn't have very many people with syphilis and malaria in your practice. So you had no curative drugs. You could buy something like aspirin tablets after World War I, but the doctor gave you powders. He put your powders, mostly acetanilide, in a folded piece of paper. Patients were to take a dose of pain powder equivalent to the amount that could rest on the end of a knife blade. If you were a seriously ill patient, he just gave you morphine tablets. That's all the doctors had.

The First Antibiotics

In 1937 real treatment started in medicine with the arrival of antibiotics. At that time bacteriology took a huge step forward. When they found out that we had drugs that could be used to kill bacteria, then they started culturing bacteria. If you had a sore throat, if you had something in your nose, or if you had a cough, they cultured you. If you had a wound that looked infected, they took a swab out of that, put it on a test plate, and cultured it for 48 hours. They grew the bacteria and then conducted sensitivity tests. That brought medicine into a totally new phase. The culturing of bacteria and conducting of sensitivity tests all began in the 1930s.

Before 1937 the greatest killers of young people were measles, whooping cough, and blood poisoning from staph or strep bacterial infections. If a wound wasn't cleaned with antiseptic carefully and staph or strep got in even a tiny wound, there was no treatment for it. If the patient's immune system did not take care of the disease, then he or she died. My father's sister died from blood poisoning when she was nineteen and my youngest sister died from blood poisoning in 1937, just a few months before sulfanilamide came out. If sulfanilamide had been in existence, she probably would have gotten over it in four or five days.

Sulfanilamide came on the market in July of 1937. It was the first of the drugs that could counteract the bacteria that were seen in cultures taken from people's wounds, noses, or throats. That was the first drug that would help when someone had a bad infection. It would take care of strep or staph and those were your worst infections. That's what killed practically everybody—strep, staph, and pneumococcus. Pneumococcus is what they use to vaccinate for pneumonia now, but when sulfanilamide came out, that was the first real antibacterial medication a doctor could give to help a patient, besides arsenic and quinine. Then the next few years, other companies developed other sulfa drugs that worked the same way. All those were developed quickly, right up to the beginning of World War II; then came penicillin.

Penicillin had been discovered a good many years before. Just by chance, a bacteriologist discovered that bacteria wouldn't grow on a test plate that had penicillin mold on it. Then somebody got the bright idea that if it kills bacteria on the plate, it'll kill germs in humans. The sulfa drugs didn't kill the germs. They simply did something to the bacteria that stopped it from causing toxic end products. But penicillin and the next drugs that came out actually killed the bacteria or stopped its growth in the bloodstream and your body then could take over and cure the infection. No doctor had the use of penicillin until about 1944. You still had to stick with the sulfa drugs, because the armed services were using all of the penicillin that could be produced.

I saw penicillin right before I left the medical college at Kirksville in 1944. They were able to get some for their serious infections like diphtheria or meningitis that were likely to be fatal to the patient. If the physicians could certify that the infection could prove fatal, they could obtain limited amounts of penicillin from a distribution center. Penicillin had to be given every three hours then. By the end of the war, they had developed it to the point that it could be given daily. They've now refined it to the point where you can give an injection of penicillin now that will last maybe a week, at least at the highest dosage level. I was able to get penicillin when I started practicing in Mullens in 1945. I was able to get some from Beckley Hospital. You had to order it from a hospital, not a drug store. Within a year or two after that, it was available through the drug companies, wholesale, from your pharmaceutical company representative.

So after 1937 people could expect some effective treatment when they went to the doctor for many illnesses and diseases, with the exception of measles, mumps, and whooping cough. Now there was also nothing for mental illness until the work of the Menninger Clinic in Kansas and the Still-Hildreth Osteopathic Sanatorium in Macon, Missouri, because they treated the patient with diet, exercise, and psychiatry.

The Dangers of Pill Popping

After penicillin came teramycin [oxytetracyclin], streptomycin, and chloromycin. For whooping cough they finally found an antibiotic - chloromycin. When it first came out, doctors used it for other infections, but it would kill the patient about as quickly as it would kill the infection. Parke-Davis had to take it off the market because it caused aplastic anemia, which occurs when your body won't make any more red blood cells. When you run out of them, if you don't get a blood transfusion, you'll die. You can keep those patients alive maybe three or four years with transfusions, but they eventually die. Aplastic anemia was known before that, but after chloromycin came out, many new cases were reported.

Most of those who died were doctors who used chloromycin to treat themselves every time they felt a little bit bad. It was such a fine drug that they just took a capsule. One of my best friends, who graduated the year before me, died from taking chloromycin. His wife said that every time he thought he was coming down with something during the winter he took two or three capsules.

Parke-Davis took chloromycin off the market for a good while, but when it turned out to be the only cure for whooping cough and typhoid fever they made it available again. You can cure either one of those in a week's time. Parke-Davis just gives you a week's supply of it now, and it specifically tells you to use it only for those two things. It's the only specific drug that will cure typhoid fever. If a patient is diagnosed with typhoid fever you just have to give the patient one prescription for a few days of treatment. So even though it caused some deaths it was an excellent drug when used with appropriate precautions for specific potentially lethal infections.

Then came Keflex and auramycin. Erythromycin was one of the ones that followed penicillin and chloromycin. There are generations of those [drugs], because the bacteria become resistant to them over time, and new generations must be developed for people who take antibiotics promiscuously. I talk to them about it every day, and you can't convince a patient. Nine out of ten of are told, "You don't have a fever. Don't use an antibiotic. Just take aspirin, drink plenty of water, rest, and you'll get better. You don't have a strep infection."

"Well, if you give me a prescription, I'll follow what you say." You find out they go straight to the drugstore, fill that prescription, and start taking it within six hours.

You tell them, "The bacteria that you have will become resistant to antibiotics if you overuse those medications. If you get a strep infection on your skin or in your lungs next month, and your body has developed bacteria resistant to all the antibiotics you have fed it, antibiotics aren't going to do any good when you need them most. Do you understand what the unnecessary overuse of antibiotics will do?" They don't seem to realize.

What people don't realize is that one bacterium can reproduce fifteen or twenty generations in one night. They think it takes a long time for those bacteria to become resistant. Have you had enough biology to understand that? They'll mutate and if you have fifteen generations in the morning, you'll have a generation growing there that your antibiotic can't fight. That's why the drug companies have to work their heads off to manufacture antibiotics that will stay ahead of that curve of resistance.

Viruses

When they began culturing for bacteria in the thirties, it was obvious that measles, chicken pox, and flu were not caused by bacteria, because they couldn't culture anything. Then they realized that they were viruses. Before that, scientists knew only that there was some agent that would pass through a certain type of pottery filter, one that would normally filter out all bacteria, and that that agent would still make people sick.

You know, to date we don't have a cure that will have any effect on a virus. And the theory is, and I totally agree with it, that as long as you don't have antibiotics in your body, you are carrying many bacteria that keep the viruses at bay. Really, when I was in school, the only virus you heard tell of was the ones that caused measles and chicken pox. Measles is viral. Chicken pox is viral. Chicken pox and shingles are the same virus. The theory was that the virus couldn't grow in the presence of the bacteria. When you take antibiotics, you kill all the normal bacteria, the natural immune flora that your body has, and then viruses take over. So really the fewer antibiotics you take, the better your chance of having a good result when you do take them. I believe what I am saying because I rarely take an antibiotic unless I have a fever that doesn't respond to large quantities of water and aspirin or acetaminophen. If you take it only when you need it, you won't harm your immune system.

We think the reason there are so many more viruses now than before is that we have extremely valuable bacteria, as well as harmful ones, and with antibiotics we killed enough of the good bacteria that fed on viruses.

There were vaccines for some viruses back in the teens. A vaccine works because a little bit of the disease is put in your body and then your immune system wipes it out. Your immune system remembers that virus and is trained to wipe it out the next time you get it. I would say the first vaccine that ever came out after smallpox was typhoid, because they gave the typhoid vaccine to soldiers for World War I. Smallpox, typhoid, and malaria killed nine out of ten people before the advent of modern medicine. I was in the ROTC or CMTC [Citizens' Military training Camps] in the summers of 1924 and 1925 in Camp Knox, Kentucky, and I had to have it. The first smallpox vaccine was not an injectible vaccine. It was just a scratch. The first injectible one I would say is the typhoid vaccine. I remember having to take three typhoid shots in 1924 and they made you sick and made your arm sore. Dr. Norman Price gave them to me.

They found the measles virus and made the measles vaccine for both types of measles. But they haven't found an antibiotic for measles. Until the mid 1990s there hasn't been an antibiotic that would do anything for a virus. Shingles is the one now that they have an antibiotic for.

Just Go Live with the Doctor

I read recently that until about 1914, if you were not going to a doctor for a surgical visit, for a fracture or a tooth extraction, you were just as well off to stay at home. You were no better after the visit than you were before. The physician Oliver Wendell Holmes—the father of the Supreme Court justice of the same name—in his time made the statement, "If you took all medicines made in this country and threw them into the ocean, the people would be much better and the fish would be much worse." There was no medicine for anything until World War I, other than anesthetics, antiseptics, arsenic, bismuth, and quinine.

Back then, you could be a medical doctor by going through the preceptor system. In other words, if there was a good doctor in your community and you wanted to be a doctor, you bought your bag and you went and lived with him for the next couple of years. You went on calls with him, helped him deliver babies, and watched what he did in surgery. The board would admit you to licensure even if you had never been in medical school.

Until after World War I most states did not require medical doctors to be licensed. Prior to 1900 most states did not have licensing boards. At the beginning of World War I, I would estimate that fifty percent of the doctors had never been to medical school. They were preceptor-trained or just self-trained. Many of the physicians who were preceptor-trained were good physicians, but they didn't have a good background in anatomy or physiology and they didn't have any background in microbiology. However, they were trained with the mentor-doctor in the technique of taking care of patients. They learned through watching. In those days there wasn't really any scientific basis for practicing.

Until World War I lots of the doctors in West Virginia were preceptor-trained or else they just took up medicine before the medical licensing board was established in this state. Before 1890 if you wanted to practice medicine, you just put a sign up outside that you were going to doctor. Believe it or not, when I went into practice in 1945 in Mullens as a coal company doctor, many salesmen told me they still called on doctors in southern West Virginia, eastern Kentucky, western North Carolina, and eastern Tennessee who had never been in medical school. And they said that many of those physicians were good doctors who were preceptor-trained or who had just read about medicine on their own.

Medical School in 1900

However, back in 1900 you could go to medical school for a few terms if you wanted to. This country was loaded with proprietary medical schools. Dr. Jim Price told me he went two terms to Baltimore College of Physicians and Surgeons and you could quit at any time you felt you knew enough to pass the board. Back then, the boards didn't require much more than two or three questions. When Dr. Price went to Baltimore there were a half-dozen or more medical schools there, and you could attend all of them if you wanted to. If you had twenty five or fifty dollars, you could register at all of them. You could get certificates from them for a two-month or six-month course of study as long as you went to lectures. There wasn't any dissection or anything like that. Scientific people gave the lectures, but they just lectured on general medicine - how to treat pneumonia, measles, and whooping cough; how to deliver a baby and how to set broken bones. That was about all they did.

My grandfather went a couple of terms to night medical school. He had gotten a certificate in Washington, D.C., and made an appointment with the West Virginia medical licensing board, which had only been in existence five years. He travelled down to Ronceverte to talk to the board, which was only one man. That member of the board asked him a question or two and wrote him a certificate to practice medicine in 1895. That was how medicine was. He never trained under another doctor.

Actually, though, doctors were doing a safer obstetrical practice in 1900 than they are now. All you did was wait for the baby to come, tie the cord, and wash the eyes, particularly if the woman had no swelling and a normal urinalysis and blood pressure. Giving birth is a physiological condition, not a pathological one [In other words, childbirth is not a sickness]. After all the babies I delivered, I had to go to medical conventions in recent years to learn that it's now considered pathological!

Just before the 1900s states had begun creating examining boards that would examine a doctor before he got his license. For years and years there was nothing like that. Those boards were very poor because they didn't have any standards. As my grandfather said, he met with only one doctor. He told my grandfather to sit down and write how he would tell if the patient had pneumonia and how he would treat it. That's all they had. Today the examinations are so complex, they give them in three parts - at the end of the first two years of medical school, at the end of the second two years, and at the end of the internship or residency. About one-third of the class pass the whole board the first time and the rest of the class has to take parts again, usually in one or two subjects.

When I was starting out the school I went to in Missouri was still only requiring two years of pre-med and four years of medicine. Schools didn't require four years of medical training until about 1916. You just went into practice when you felt you were ready. And believe it or not, we use the term *doctor* now when we graduate. In the old schools you were *bachelor of medicine*—in Europe, you can practice with just four years of training—and back then the term "doctor" was just picked up for those trained by medical lecturers or through a preceptorship. That's a little bit on the history of medicine.

The Flexner Report

About 1910 a doctor named Flexner recognized how bad the licensure system actually was. You've heard of Abraham Flexner and the Flexner Report if you know anything about medical history. He started looking at medical schools all over the country and there were hundreds of them that didn't really have any campus or anything. Every city of any size had a half-dozen or more places where you could get a certificate to be a doctor. Flexner set up an inspection and review process, with the approval of the American Medical Association, to examine these institutions. They made a tour of many in the United

States. Then Flexner wrote a report to the American Medical Association, to the medical schools, and to the states that had medical licensing boards.

That report started a medical revolution. The diploma mills or proprietary institutions really went out of business and the colleges and universities became more conscious of this need. They tried to absorb the institutions, consolidate them, and incorporate them under colleges and universities to award legitimate certificates for the practice of medicine. The legitimate medical schools created a national accrediting body. That was the establishment of accreditation and from then on medical schools had to meet certain requirements. The diploma mills had to shut down because they had no real facilities and no faculty other than two or three doctors who collected fees and gave casual lectures on general medicine. It was a good money-making business. There are still diploma mills. The Philippines are full of them. The medical profession in this country has never really been truthful and said that. Most of the public hospitals in West Virginia were staffed up until recent years by unlicensed physicians. A lot of the veterans' hospitals and state-supported institutions could use those people without a license if they had one doctor on the staff that was licensed to sign for everything. That may still be happening.

After 1910 and the Flexner Report, everything began to be upgraded. Medicine became a four-year course of study by 1916. Before that, it could be one year or whatever the institution stipulated. After 1916 you did not have to have pre-med, but you did have to have four years of medical school. Now, the diploma mills would take students at any time during the year, but the universities would take a class of students. At first they just accepted the first forty or fifty students who applied. In the 1920s medical schools started interviewing and screening their candidates. By the 1930s, when you graduated from medical school, you had to complete an internship that gave you experience in a hospital after medical school.

After the Flexner Report, institutions were inspected. Until the 1930s medical schools were either class A, class B, or class C schools. Then they slowly put everyone out of business that wasn't a class A medical school. Most states passed resolutions that you could not be licensed unless you graduated from a class A school of medicine. There were several things that influenced a school's classification. It could have been poorly qualified students, a poorly credentialed faculty, a lack of medical facilities or laboratories, or that the school lacked a certain curriculum. A lot of them weren't teaching dissection at all. They didn't have the bodies to teach it and they didn't go to the trouble of getting them because cadavers are expensive and difficult to acquire. So the authorities just gradually cut out the schools that didn't meet all of the qualifications.

Every medical school operating in the United States today is a Class A medical school. For ordinary people just going to the doctor, I don't think these changes made any difference at all until those doctors who were preceptor-trained, self-trained, or had come through a diploma mill died out and all the practicing graduates were from Class A medical schools. Medicine became reasonably good between World War I and the 1930s. It would not become uniform until all of those old doctors passed away or had retired from practice.

Scarcity and Surplus

After World War I schools began to require a little pre-med and by the 1930s they had set up committees to review the students who were applying. Well, when I started to medical school the entrance requirements were just about what they are now. There's been very little change in entrance requirements. After 1938 pre-medical requirements changed from two years pre-med to a minimum of three years, but the subjects required have not changed since 1930. During World War II it was only two years, because doctors were in such demand. Most any medical school in this country today will admit you with three years if you're an unusual student, but their requirements will be four years of pre-med. That really doesn't make for a better doctor. It does make for a more mature student, because with no pre-med you got a younger graduate who might be less committed.

Then by 1950, after World War II, there were so many applicants for medical school that they had to have an admissions director and an application committee to select those to be interviewed. For example, when I entered Morgantown, I don't know how many applicants they had, but they must not have had many because the man who interviewed me said, "When you arrange it, you can be admitted this fall." No school tells that now. With our first class at the school in Lewisburg, students didn't even know if the accrediting body was really going to permit us to open, yet we had four hundred applications for thirty six places. After that year, we had our own application committee, and we received eight hundred applications for thirty six places. The class of 2000 had seventy places. They had something like 1,420 applications. So you see it's a real problem.

That started after World War II. More people were going to college and more were taking pre-med. The war proved that we didn't have nearly enough doctors. Practically all the eligible doctors were drafted. Nothing but a bunch of old leftovers remained to take care of 100,000,000 people who were left in this country. It got to be tragic how few doctors were left here. That was due strictly to the American Medical Association [AMA}. The AMA was a political organization that paid very little attention, at least until after the Flexner Report, to medical schools at all. After they began to pay attention to the medical schools, they decided about how many doctors they wanted to graduate per year. So they cut the number of applicants to the medical schools so they could have a graduating class that could be managed by the AMA, which would control the income of doctors.

The scarcity was planned by the AMA so that doctors' incomes would increase, because doctors had little income during the Depression. That plan went down the drain with the war. I was going to say that the AMA would dispute what I'm saying about a planned scarcity, but there aren't enough of them still living now to dispute me. In other words, they were operating a planned scarcity of physicians before the war started and right through the Depression. When the war started, there was a real planned scarcity. The medical schools were not taking nearly as many as they could educate because the AMA said, "We will not accredit you if you take more." That's why WVU in Morgantown, where I started medical school, only took thirty two students. They told us when I interviewed there, "We may only be able to keep twenty of you for the second class. It just depends on what the AMA committee on accreditation tells us." After the war, the AMA's inspection committee became much more liberal.

Foreign Diploma-Mill Doctors

We ran into a major scarcity of doctors when they were all taken into the service during the wars. The hospitals in this country took many physicians that came from the Philippines, Mexico, and the Middle East. It didn't matter what training they had. [Federal legislation in 1940 and 1948 facilitated the entry of physicians from abroad.] That's how this country was flooded with those diploma-mill doctors. Every big hospital in this country took them. Anybody who said they had graduated from any medical school anywhere in the world could come to America and get a job, because we lacked a quarter of a million doctors.

When the war was going on, we got many doctors from other countries. We didn't have any doctors coming from countries like England, Germany, Norway, and Sweden—all of which had good systems of medical education. They needed them in their own country. India flooded this country. You can't go anywhere now that you won't find an Indian doctor, because they were oversupplied with medical schools. Some were diploma-mill doctors and some were real. Nobody who graduated in India wanted to stay in India, because there they had to practice for nothing, so many of them wanted to come to this country because of the superior income. After the war, there was a big push for medical schools to admit more students, to train American physicians to replace these foreign doctors.

In the late 1950s or '60s our country began to press down on foreign doctors coming into the United States from diploma mills. They made them take an examination called the ECFMG [Educational Commission for Foreign Medical Graduates]. That was a board set up to examine everybody who came from a foreign country before they could take the regular medical licensing board exams. Now, they didn't have to have the ECFMG board before they went to work in public institutions, but before they could take the licensing board, they had to take the ECFMG. That had to show that they could speak English well enough, that they had four years of proper medical training, and that they had passed the basic subjects. Less than fifty percent of those taking it, at least as long as I was associated with the examination, could even pass the ECFMG.

Now, when you go in a big medical center, you don't know if the doctor who comes in to treat you was trained in India, the Philippines, Mexico, or the Caribbean, because 150,000 of our 600,000 doctors are those diploma-mill doctors. West Virginia's loaded with them. If you go into hospital, unless you know a doctor you have been referred to, you may be sent to anybody. And I'm going to add this - some of those doctors who were trained in India and at the three medical schools in the Philippines that were set up by the United States when the U.S. owned the Philippines are just as good as ours over here. But your problem is that in some cases the social attitudes of an Indian or someone from the Middle East are nothing like ours.

For instance, I'll describe what I overheard down here one time when they had a surgeon from the Middle East here in Marlinton. One of my patients had undergone surgery and he later developed a post-surgical infection that lingered along for three or four weeks. He died one night and the surgeon came in. I said, "Mr. So-and-So died last night." He said, "Good. That's fine. That patient was 56 years old. He'd lived his life." He just went on with his day. That was his social attitude. If you have a sick baby in there, why waste your time? Sick babies—they're expendable in some societies. You don't know the social attitude of foreign-trained peoples. That's why I always tell people to ask if their doctor has been trained in the United States, Canada, Europe, Israel. If he came from England, Germany, Sweden, or Norway, you might accept him as well-trained. Otherwise you don't know what you're getting. I sound like an old, disgruntled man.

Preventive Medicine

Preventive medicine is a recent concept in allopathic [conventional] medicine, but it was part of osteopathic medicine from the beginning. Structural integrity and natural immunity—the two key principles of osteopathy—are all about preventive medicine.

After physicians got antiseptics, anesthetics, antibiotics, and the drugs for mental illnesses that came in the late fifties, preventive medicine came into the forefront. Then doctors began to talk about wellness programs and illness prevention. We began to talk about weight, vitamins, exercise, food that you ate, and beginning in the seventies we became cholesterol conscious. Biochemistry reached the point where scientists could test a wide variety of substances that are found in the blood.

When I went to medical school, all they did were blood sugars, blood urea nitrogen, creatinine, and other simple blood counts. That's all they did. Now they have a hundred different tests. They have isolated so many different enzymes from your blood that you could be tested for a hundred things. They found out that the absence or presence of too much of certain enzymes could be responsible for your immune system not being able to fight off various diseases. So that's when the wellness program came in. They have begun to test routinely for cholesterol, glucose, triglycerides, low-density lipoproteins, high-density lipoproteins, very-low-density lipoproteins—testing for all of that because they then isolated the covering of the inside of blood vessels that causes arteriolosclerosis and associated that immediately with cholesterol. It was either calcium or cholesterol, so now they do the calcium, sodium, and potassium, as well as the cholesterols. If you have arteriolosclerosis, they try to determine whether the disease is related to cholesterol or calcium problems.

Of course, then they found that too much calcium in your blood might be the cause of osteoporosis. If your blood calcium is too high, it's not from your intake of calcium. Your body is taking the calcium out of your bones, transporting it into your blood, and purging it through the kidneys. Their first thought was to give calcium supplements to these people. They found that giving calcium supplements didn't lower the blood calcium at all. The body just purged the extra calcium. Scientists then learned that you have to have vitamin D before your body can absorb the calcium. All doctors were told to give vitamin D. That helped a little bit, but they also found that the combination of vitamin D, calcium, and exercise worked the best. The exercise helped your body. Exercise stimulates the immune system to permit the body to better absorb the calcium. Now they have found enzymes that you take every day to prevent your body from extracting the calcium from your bones. This helps prevent osteoporosis. Hormones have something to do with that, because they found out that women do not develop osteoporosis until after menopause, but that didn't explain it in men. Men get osteoporosis, but only about a fourth as frequently as women.

The Origins of Osteopathy

The difference between osteopathic medicine and traditional medicine was stated simply by Dr. Andrew Taylor Still, founder of the profession, in 1874. This statement is even more important today. He said, "Health depends upon the structural integrity of your body and the natural immunity." Most doctors didn't know what he was talking about. They'd never heard of structural integrity. The term "structural integrity" was not used in medical schools. Where he got that term God only knows, but he meant that if you had any defect, it would affect you. Certain people sit with their head turned to the side. Some people have one leg shorter than the other. He said, "If that is not corrected, it influences your internal organs, and if your internal organs are affected, then your natural immunity is affected." It's been proven true. That's why there are twenty five osteopathic medical schools in the United States.

Medical doctors, one or two of them, began to look at that idea back in the thirties and forties. One wrote a book about the somatic symptoms of visceral pathology. This theory contends that internal health issues manifest themselves in symptoms that show outwardly. In other words if you have a peptic ulcer, there will be some externally discernible symptoms. Osteopathically, they found that the fourth thoracic vertebra would be a trigger point for pain in patients with peptic ulcers. Those who had tuberculosis had certain defects in the upper thoracic area of the body. Dr. Still's theories are now quoted in medical circles all over the world. Then, of course, no one believed him. It was like Semmelweis talking about bacteria. The pain in the back is real. I have patients come in and say, "I think I have kidney trouble or something like that. I have had a pain in my back for four or five days." Forty to fifty percent of the time, that pain comes from colitis or irritable colon syndrome, or something wrong in the bowel that is reflected in the skeletal system, the somatic system. And that's the difference between osteopathic medicine and traditional medicine, but it's all going to be the same eventually because everyone accepts those osteopathic principles now.

Natural immunity—you hear that in everything you read now. And Dr. Still used that term in 1874. It's published. He was a preceptor-trained doctor who only had one year of training at Kansas City University of Physicians and Surgeons. The reason he did not have more was that his father was a preceptor-trained doctor who was a Methodist medical missionary to the Indians. His father took Still along and taught him medicine. Then the father sent his son for one year to Kansas City. After that, Dr. Still became a real medical philosopher and eventually established the first osteopathic school of medicine.

It was all founded on that seminal statement that he made - The good health of a patient depends upon structural integrity and natural immunity. All the doctors who worked with Dr. Still to start the first osteopathic school were M.D.s, as was Dr. Still. Now, whenever you go to a medical lecture, they talk about those two ideas—whether it's an M.D. or a D.O. who's doing the talking. They always talk about immune systems being upset. Nobody knew about immune systems until Dr. Still came along! Had he been a physician in Baltimore, Boston, or even Chicago, he would have been world-famous fifty or a hundred years before this. It's just because he was out in Missouri, Kansas, and Nebraska among the Indians that he wasn't better known. Now what most people don't know is that doctors used to say that this old guy Still was a quack!

He and his father were [among] the founders of Baker University in Baldwin [City], Kansas, back when they were missionaries to the Indians out there. It's a Methodist school that Robert Taylor, the movie actor, graduated from. So the Stills were education-minded people. They weren't just two men out being missionaries and practicing quackery.

That first osteopathic school of medicine at Kirksville was established by a full faculty of M.D.s. And the chairman of the Department of Anatomy at the Kirksville school, William Smith, was an Edinburgh graduate. The first class of graduates completed the curriculum in two years. From the beginning the school had two years of dissection. Dr. Smith used to say he got tired of going to medical meetings and hearing everyone call osteopaths a bunch of quacks. He decided to go see for himself—it took him a week in a horse and buggy to go the 250 miles to Kirksville. When he returned he said, "The old quack is curing a lot of people!" So many people were traveling to Kirksville that the Wabash Railroad had to put an extra train on the line!

The degrees conferred were not "Doctor of Medicine." That's something that we just evolved into. It was a "Diplomate of Medicine." So the Missouri Medical Board more or less informed the new school that they weren't going to let their graduates sit for the licensing board. So the doctors who established the school said, "Well, we'll just grant them Diplomates of Medicine of Osteopathy." That's where the D.O. came from. And that way, we didn't have to take the M.D. board exam.

The Philosophy of the Osteopath

After my graduation from medical school and learning the philosophy of osteopathic medicine and traditional medical education, I was totally sold on the philosophy of the osteopathic method. At that time, there were three systems of education - osteopathic medical, homeopathic medical, and traditional medical education. Osteopathic medical education embraced natural immunity, which wasn't even taught in traditional medicine for years. Today that's all you hear; your body's natural immunity. That principle was adopted and established in osteopathic medicine in 1874. Today there are only two systems, and they are getting more and more alike all the time. Traditional medical education has accepted osteopathic medical education principles. From the beginning osteopathic medicine accepted the principles of traditional medicine. We just expanded upon them.

Now there are twenty five schools of osteopathic medicine. There were only six when I started. Some of the leading universities such as Rutgers, Michigan State, Ohio University in Athens, Oklahoma State University, North Texas University, and Nova [Southeastern] University all have schools of osteopathic medicine. Pikeville College in Pikeville, Kentucky is only three or four years old [this interview was in 2001], but it has become very popular because of their philosophy of treating sick people and their reputation for treating patients with compassion.

The AMA is much more conservative. That's why the osteopathic schools of medicine have experienced such enormous growth. It's the fastest growing health profession ever in existence because, except for the accrediting body, they are more liberal in their thoughts. The American Osteopathic Association [AOA] did not fight Social Security. They did not go on record against Medicare. The AMA fought Social Security and Medicare to the dead end. They were still voting against Medicare when Congress passed it, and our group shut up years before because they could see it coming. Nearly everything, except in the field of research, that comes out in the AMA has been proposed first by the AOA.

I'm not running any medical school down. I feel that they are all compassionate in their own ways, but I feel that the philosophy of osteopathy is very patient-centric. In osteopathic medical education, we were taught, "Don't talk down to your patients. You're talking to a human spirit just like yourself. Treat them the same way you would want to be treated, and always consider that natural immunity is what gets you well, not the pill you take. The medicine you take might reinforce your natural immunity, but a lot of medicine you take lowers your natural immunity." I don't know if you realize it or not, but every time you take an antibiotic, it lowers your natural

Dr. Sharp being examined by a young patient at his Green Bank clinic - 1970s.

immunity. We became human beings, civilized human beings, long before there were any doctors, any medicine, or anything like that. Your body has a series of natural systems that could make you immune to diseases or at least resistant to many. Through, I guess, survival of the fittest, people grew to what they are now.

If you're going to medical school for social prestige, go to an M.D. school. If you want to be in certain high-tech specialties, go to the M.D. school. If you really want to be a doctor, a general family doctor, go to an osteopathic school. These days, D.O.s can do anything. You can graduate from this school in Lewisburg and take your residency at Harvard. It's acceptable. People didn't know that when I was in school.

Bureaucracy & Greed Advance

"You were much safer to have a serious accident or a serious surgery in the sixties than you are today."

"Now they have more complicated ways of diagnosis. We're so technologically ahead of the treatment that it's unbelievable. I think it'll just have to keep getting worse until it gets better."

"Patients just don't seem to matter anymore—they are lost in the bureaucracy and the greed."

—Roland Sharp

A lot of good people go into medicine, but money seems to be discussed too much. It's probably hard for you to believe, but I went to medical school for four years and never heard money discussed once. I heard a doctor or two come in who had graduated and say, "If you will come into my community, I feel sure you can make $350.00 a month." That's all I heard. I never heard any professor say anything about dollars and cents.

I think to be a good doctor you first have to be compassionate and be interested in people. When we entered medical school, one of the main things we were told was that it was a privilege to be a doctor and not a right. I used to remind students that four or five other prospective students were being rejected for every one accepted. As a medical student and one who was privileged to be a doctor, one had certain responsibilities. Those responsibilities were to take care of everybody in the community regardless of whether they could pay or not. You needed to recognize that anywhere you went into practice there would be a certain number of people who would not be able to pay. You had to accept that and recognize that you were part of a community. You had to give the same good care to those less fortunate that you gave to the people who could pay.

These days, doctors are not taught that. This is a different generation. I'm not saying it's worse. I don't believe that. I think that there are a lot of good people going into medicine now, but it seems that the attitudes have changed remarkably. I think most students, or at least half of the students who go to medical school today, go because it's a profitable business. When I went to school, I had no idea whether it would be a profitable business or not. My grandfather was a doctor and he hardly made enough to live on. I went, in part, because I was teaching school and teaching certainly wasn't a profitable business. As a teacher, you didn't know one year if you were going to have a job the next year.

Doctors' attitudes have changed. What egged that on, partly, is that we had a group of young people, a generation of them who entered the profession in the sixties, who couldn't see that things were pretty good the way they were. They wanted to revolutionize. They helped some things, but they helped destroy family medicine. They developed a generation of people who said, "You owe yourself something."

In other words, when I was educated and got a license and set out to practice, you felt that you owed the patient. That was your first priority, not your family or whether you wanted to go to a concert. When you took that Hippocratic oath—and the osteopathic oath was even more binding—you pledged yourself to do everything you could for the patient regardless whether it was day, night, time for Christmas dinner, your anniversary, or whatever. The patient always had to come first. When I started practice, every doctor followed that oath. I don't think I practiced in a community where anyone who graduated prior to World War II or during the war, didn't do that. Now, they take off any day they want to take off. That's not all of them. Half of the class will be just as dedicated as my generation ever was, but the other half has the attitude that patients are secondary.

"They'll be sick tomorrow just as well as today. If they're going to get well, they're going to get well. If they're not going to get well, then they can get attention somewhere else."

What the medical school admissions committee tries to determine, aside from your grades is "Are you a person with a conscience. Are you socially inclined?" I mean, when a doctor interviews a patient, does the patient's welfare come first? Or is it a very high priority? I don't think it should come above your family, if you have an illness in your own family, but I think it should come above family holidays and concerts and things like that. A patient's life should be a high enough priority to miss those things. I missed Christmas dinner, I don't know how many times, to deliver a baby and such. I don't think there are many doctors who will do that now. They'll say, "Give her a shot to stop her pains for a few hours" or "I'll refer her to the next hospital where they can do a C-section."

That attitude changed in doctors because a moral and social change took place. I don't know why. Many medical schools just quit teaching it. The older doctors used to teach you those things, that you were responsible. Then you get a younger person who says, "Well, to a point." Then you get another generation that says, "Well, I need to come first."

When people talk with me, they might say, "You still think young" or "You still defend the present generation," and I do. I think the medical world will get better, but I think we went through some kind of a social change in the sixties.

Medicare Takes Over Hospitals

There's something else that I have been very worried about. I think government interference in medicine has changed medicine from compassionate medicine to corporate medicine. And those two terms mean something totally different. Before World War II medical schools, hospitals, and clinics were owned by the people, the doctors, or the community. Hospitals were not organizations seeking to make money. They were a workshop for the doctor, just like a good mechanic would like to have a building where he could work out of the weather. Doctors built hospitals so that they could bring patients in and give them care in one place instead of going out to everyone's home. You might have to be at someone's home two or three days. Hospitals were doctor's workshops, not profit centers. The doctor's fee was where he made his money.

Well, the government started to change that when Medicare came into existence. Everything after that was about money. I'll give you a little example; our local hospital. When I joined the staff in 1963, Mr. Clyde Cochran was the administrator. It cost $49.40 to spend the night in that hospital. It was full of people. It was paying its way, Mr. Cochran told me.

But Medicare was beginning. The government was sending the older patient a Medicare card. Our hospital was not accredited for Medicare. As the patients came in, they had this Medicare card and they thought this meant free treatment. It looked good on paper. People on Medicare came to Mr. Cochran and said, "You ought to sign up for Medicare. They pay seventy-nine dollars per day." And patients who came in said, "Well, I'm going to go to Ronceverte or maybe to Elkins or wherever there is a Medicare hospital, because they'll pay for us."

Eventually Mr. Cochran said, "Well, I guess we're going to have to sign up for Medicare or we're going to lose patients." So we signed up for Medicare and we kept our patients. But just as soon as we were signed with Medicare, they sent a group of administrative people in, not doctors, a couple of nurses or two, maybe one doctor to start with, to look things over. Well, the hospital was accredited. They had no real business there, but Medicare said, "We have to inspect your hospital."

The first thing they said was, "Who is your pharmacist?" We said, "The doctor just writes down what he wants, and the head nurse goes up to the pharmacy, and they fix up the medicine and send it back to the nurse's station. The nurse's station has a cabinet where they lock it up." The head nurse kept the key in her pocket.

Medicare said, "You can't do that. You have to have a pharmacist." Well, the hospital had to hire a pharmacist and the job paid eight or ten thousand dollars a year.

The next thing they asked was, "Where is your supply room?" We go down to the supply room.

"Who operates the supply room?"

"The head nurse. The doctors write what they want in the way of bandages, sutures, tape, and all that, and the head nurse goes with a cart to the supply room. She puts all that on the cart and brings it up to the nurse's station, and the doctor uses it."

"You can't do that. You can't be a Medicare hospital. You have to have that supply room staffed every day."

Mr. Cochran said, "That won't be a problem. We can get someone to stay down there. But we don't need it. That's a waste of money."

Medicare said, "One! You have to have three. It has to be open twenty four hours a day—three eight-hour shifts." So now we had to have people who just sit there in the supply room and who do nothing else whatsoever. The nurse still goes down. And the people in the supply room help put the supplies on the cart, but now there are three more people getting paid. In just a short time, the salaries were already taking up that seventy-nine dollars!

Another thing Medicare looked at was the elevator. They said, "This elevator won't do. You have to have another elevator." The elevator problem was argued back and forth with Medicare for ten or twelve years. You know what happened right at the last? The State administration changed, a Republican came in, and they changed fire marshals. When the new fire marshal came to the hospital, the board told him, "We have been trying to figure out where to put an elevator. We were told by Medicare this one is too small and that we can't put a larger one here because it will create a fire hazard. We don't know where to put it."

The new fire marshal said, "What's wrong with where it is? Just put it right where it the old one is." And the new elevator went in right where the old one had been.

That is part of the reason why medical service deteriorated—why it went from an emphasis on taking care of the patients to that administrative and technical junk. Goodness only knows how much extra the hospital had to pay in salaries. They had to cut nurses and the other nurses had to do all the paperwork. At that time they were just beginning with licensed practical nurses, so the LPNs had to take over what the nurses were doing, and then the LPNs had to work so hard that they had to have aides. When I first started there was no such thing as an aide. The nurses and the nurses' assistants were attending to all of the patients.

Then the next thing they said was, "A doctor cannot collect any money from Medicare if he owns any stock in this hospital." Nurses couldn't either—nobody could. Then the hospitals had to be transferred to nonprofit corporations. This hospital was nonprofit, so the board had to be made up of lay people. They were allowed to have maybe one doctor on the board. That led to these corporations that were looking into buying hospitals. So then we had corporate hospitals. The corporate hospitals just went on a binge, buying all of nonprofits and even buying them for sale on the stock exchanges. Those hospitals were operated to make dividends for the stockholders rather than to provide for the well-being of patients.

So you can see what I'm talking about now. That's why, in many hospitals, families have to go help take care of seriously ill patients because these institutions are inadequately staffed. I would say right down here in Marlinton we have one of the best hospitals in the state as far as taking care of people. If I were sick, I would go there. Of course, it's not a surgical unit, but you will receive medical care here that is just as good as care you'd receive anywhere else.

You see, when the government pays for something everyone wants in on the gravy. They want to get in on the gravy train so they can bill the state or federal government for services. Everyone wants it. I think Medicare will never get back to a state of compassion until the hospitals and the clinics are owned and controlled by physicians, nurses, and citizens.

Then patients will be treated the way they should be treated. Now if somebody in the medical profession reads this, they'll probably take me for a complete radical. I am telling you the honest truth.

Medicare reached a place where they set up what was called the Diagnostic Related Group - DRG. That works like this; you come in with a lung problem and a group of doctors and nurses computes an average for how long a person with pneumonia will stay in the hospital for that. They say maybe three days for that. You go in the hospital with a kidney infection. They get together and say so many days is the average for that condition. Medicare says we will pay only the DRG—the dollar amount that group set. If you go in for your kidneys, you're going to stay three days unless there is something you can document as a very, very significant problem. If you go in with a heart attack, three days or four is all the hospital will be paid for. If you stay longer, the doctor can come to you and decide that you need five more days. As the doctor I will apply for five more days, but there's better than a fifty-fifty chance you'll be denied. Will you be responsible for paying the balance? You can stay as long as you want, but if Medicare says that you have to go out the third day, you will have to pay for the rest. But so many people cannot pay for it because the cost is up to several hundred dollars a day. So patients say, "Send me home." Cancer patients used to die in the hospital. Now they die at home, unless they're unconscious.

That's why hospice was set up. The hospital had been taking care of these patients and when I came to Marlinton, it cost forty five to fifty dollars a day. Patients had good care there even if they had to stay for three months. It made a considerable hospital or doctor bill, but it wasn't beyond their reach.

Medicare will pay me for one visit per day to any patient I admit. Sometimes if the patient is not acutely ill, the doctor won't get paid for more than one visit every other day. If the patient is not acutely ill, he'll probably get dumped out the second day and the doctor will get paid for one day. Before that, most of us doctors saw the patient every time we walked down the hall. You'd drop in and say, "How are you?" You might listen to their chest, feel their pulse, or check their chart and see what their temperature is, and you didn't charge six visits in there a day. That was considered a part of your duty. Today you've got so much red tape, so much paperwork to fill out. The poor doctor or nurse doesn't get a chance to go there twice unless there's a real emergency. The aide tells you what the patient said.

Years back you could treat the patient the way you thought the patient ought to be treated. In the sixties I was working on the staff of the hospital in Marlinton. I'd go in the morning and make rounds. If I had a sick patient and I was still there at noon, I'd go back and see the patient again. I'd go back to the office and if I had to go back down in the evening, I'd go back and see the patient. The patient was charged for one visit to the hospital room. Some doctors charged for all three visits, but most doctors didn't. Pretty soon Medicare came out and said, "You can't make but one room visit every other day to that patient. That patient just had a cut foot," or "That patient is just getting over pneumonia." They said, "That patient doesn't need to be seen every day."

Well, the only reason I went in there was because I felt like the patient needed to be seen. Otherwise they could go home. If I had someone in there with a wound, I didn't want to depend on the nurse to tell me whether it's infected or not. I wanted to go in there and look at it myself.

Some doctors today will send a patient out of the hospital with a temperature of 103 or 104 because the Diagnostic Related Group says, "Time's up!" The last one that I had like that, the patient went home and then the family took the patient to Allegheny Regional Hospital. They took the patient as a new admission and he stayed about two weeks due to complications from pneumonia that developed because he had to get out of the first hospital!

Patients blame the doctor and Medicare lays all that on the doctor. He's responsible for discharging that patient on the third day. If he says that patient is too sick to go and keeps him or her two extra days, Medicare doesn't pay for it. Medicare can just say to the patient, "You stayed there. You pay it." It has created that kind of attitude and the doctor is the one who has to break all that bad news to the patient. And you know what the patient thinks? He thinks the doctor can change it or that the doctor set up those rules. He really doesn't have any more say in it than one of the nurses would.

I have written letters time and again on behalf of patients. I wore myself out explaining why some patient should be in the hospital an extra day. That's when I was active on the staff. The letters usually didn't do any good. They usually gave you an 800 number to call and explain the circumstance. But you could sit at that 800 number from eight o'clock in the morning to midnight and not see a patient all day. The number will be busy all the time or they'll put you on hold and you listen to music. That's why I'm so disgusted.

We haven't used a roll of stamps to send out bills in the last ten years. The only bills we send out are the insurance and the Medicare bills and all that. You may have a ten dollar statement, and then you spend six dollars on stamps before you get them to approve it. I usually tell Barbara, my office nurse, once we do a couple, "Forget it. Just let it go, before we waste another three dollars in stamps."

Salaries on the Rise

When my grandfather was a doctor, he hardly made enough money to live on. Doctors out in communities like this were just making a living. They weren't making any more money than school teachers. The only money my grandfather made was during World War I. After the war, he did some service until he was seventy five or eighty for the Warn Lumber Corporation, and he received a little salary through that.

Doctors' incomes through the 1920s improved. But in the thirties they dropped, unless you were a surgeon. Everybody wanted to be a surgeon then. Everybody who was coming out of medical school was trying to get another year so they could do surgery, where you could earn thirty or forty dollars. Before that you know, it was fifty cents and a dollar. I can remember going to the doctor's office in Marlinton for a dollar in the thirties. Dr. Jim Price never charged more than fifty cents a visit, ten dollars for a delivery at home. If a patient had nothing, then maybe he'd give the doctor a ham or a couple of dozen eggs.

As I said, when I went to medical school, I never heard income mentioned. We knew they weren't earning much when they paid interns only twenty five dollars a month. They considered the internship part of your education. Well, it's still considered part of your education, but the lowest I've ever heard of an intern making in the last dozen years or so is twenty five thousand dollars. Most hospitals are offering thirty to thirty five thousand, and that's for an intern. You're being educated!

After the Second World War the field experienced large increases in pay. State and government fees accounted for much of the increase. I never received any pay from any agency until 1950—well, other than the coal company that paid my salary or the patient paying it out of pocket. Nobody had insurance, so there were no insurance papers to fill out.

Sometime in the forties, a Department of Welfare was created that took the poorest people in your area and gave them some type of service. They paid you for that. The fee was two dollars. That was the most they allowed. Then in two or three years some more social programs came, and they allowed you three dollars for an office visit and five dollars for a home call.

I have contended that the social programs are responsible for the high doctor charges, the high hospital charges, and the high drug charges. The doctor just automatically says, "Well, if it's coming out of the taxpayer, I'll charge five dollars." That's when you were permitted your own charge. But you're not permitted your own charge anymore. Everybody else, even insurance companies, tells you what you get.

There was a period; I'd say through the seventies, that a doctor's visit went up a dollar every year. When I first came back to Pocahontas County, a visit was three dollars. Two or three years later it was four dollars. Another year or two it was five dollars, and the insurance companies and the welfare programs were paying for that. The doctors who were doing nothing but private practice just sat there and the older doctors who weren't doing any of these welfare patients, they also just sat there and charged what the other doctors were getting.

Corporate Medicine

Health insurance for people who didn't have welfare started many years ago. Blue Cross Blue Shield was insuring a few people probably in the forties, then by the fifties they began to insure more, and then by the sixties they were insuring a lot more. When the price of an office visit was down, nobody would buy insurance. There's no reason for you to buy hospital insurance when Pocahontas Memorial charged you fifty dollars a day. That was the about the rate when I went on the staff there in 1963, and the hospital was full.

Then the hospital had to sign up with Medicare or they couldn't be paid. The next week after that, Medicare paid hospitals $79.50, and they thought, "Great!" That's what ruined everything. By the time you had all the things that Medicare wanted you to have, and all the staff, and filled out all the forms, the hospital had doubled its number of employees, so they couldn't pay them with the $79.50!

For years after that, we doctors tried to tell Medicare and the government that this was not a workable system. Doctors, hospitals, drug companies, every agency I think, were ripping off the government.

These drug companies that merge say, "We're going to do so to lower the cost of drugs, to be more efficient in our research." They don't do that for anything other than to cut down the amount of drugs they produce and cut down the number of researchers they have and up the price of drugs unbelievably, to give the stockholders more dividends. As just one example, one shot that cost seventy five cents in 1999 now costs fifteen dollars.

I have always said that when medicine became corporate instead of compassionate, it went down the drain.

Technology was advancing in medicine, but everything was becoming corporate. The high point I would say, in medical practice, was the sixties. You could examine the way you wanted, prescribe the way you wanted, and keep the patient in the hospital as long as you thought necessary. People weren't suing doctors. My malpractice insurance cost forty dollars a year in those days. Now it's $3,600 for keeping office hours three days a week—with no surgery and no emergency room work!

The insurance companies are an even bigger rip-off. The insurance companies were paying you a decent rate and they were charging patients a premium that would permit the companies to pay the doctors well and still make some money. But then Medicare said, "We are only going to pay for three days for pneumonia."

The insurance companies said, "We'll only pay three days for that too. And we won't pay you any more than Medicare rates." But even though companies lowered what they were paying doctors, they didn't drop their premiums for patients. The patients' premiums went up every year! No insurance company will pay any more than any federal or state agency will pay, and the federal and state agencies rarely pay enough for a doctor to live on. If you didn't have private patients and some tips, you probably would go under!

I think it's getting worse. The service that a patient gets in the hospital today is certainly not as good as the patient got up until the early seventies. Then you had nurses, all registered nurses. Your aide was an LPN, a licensed practical nurse. LPNs didn't even exist until the sixties. Then after that, you had a nurse, an LPN, and an LPN aide. Now they have an LPN, a nurse's aide, and then they just have girls that, I don't know what you call them, but those are the ones that are doing what your registered nurse did. When I had a kidney infection patient or a pneumonia patient in the hospital, the nurse saw them about every three hours and charted it. I would see them three times a day. You didn't have a lot of records to keep. I wish you could look at a chart today! Nurses don't have time to supervise LPNs. And the LPNs don't have time to supervise the aides, so they're all on their own. You were much safer to have a serious accident or a serious surgery in the sixties than you are today.

Now they have more complicated ways of diagnosis. We are so technologically ahead of the treatment that it's unbelievable. I think it'll just have to keep getting worse until it gets better.

A Family Doctor

I think doctors in general practice should spend their time taking care of the patient's health and they should promote everything in the community as far as they can—all the community activities like the public library, the fire department, the social organizations, or the church of their choice. A good doctor in a community will give as much as he can to any of those institutions.

Being a part of the community probably isn't part of being a good doctor, but it's a part of showing your willingness to promote the community that you live in. Anything that a doctor does that promotes the community is going to indirectly help the people. I am sure that the level of education in a community has a lot to do with the health of a community. Certainly people who read would know more about their diet, heart disease, smoking, and strokes.

A good family doctor should totally manage the patient's care. A family doctor has reasonable training in specialties of all sorts. In other words, I should be able to recognize dermatological conditions that I can't treat. I should recognize practically any surgical problem. I don't treat anything but minor surgery in the office, and that's where I stop. I know enough to refer the patient to competent surgeons.

I think the family doctor is far more qualified to tell the patient where to go than the patient is to pick his own specialist or hospital, because patients pick physicians according to the doctor's personality, not according to the quality of medicine that the doctor practices. If he is a good public relations person, he'll have patients following him like the Pied Piper. It has nothing to do with quality at all. Your family doctor knows the quality because he refers patients to this one, that one, another one. He gets reports. If he's got good sense, he can read the reports and tell if he's referred the patient to the proper doctor.

On the other hand, there are too many specialists. I get so disgusted. If you send a patient to one specialist and the patient asks the doctor about something else, instead of giving them an answer, they say, "See your doctor." Everybody should have a family doctor they can talk to, who refers them where they need to go. The problem with people today is they want to choose their own practice, manage their own care, go to see the specialist they think they ought to see, instead of seeing a family doctor and learning whether they really need specialty care. MRIs cost $4,000 to $5,000. It isn't unusual to see two or three patients a week who walk in the office and say, "I want to be referred somewhere for an MRI." What do you think that does to the cost of medicine if the doctor refers the patient? That's why it's billions and billions of dollars, and it's going to multiply every year.

Advertising

A doctor who wants people to know that he's a specialist is supposed to put out an announcement. He can put notices in the paper that he is specializing in a field. But he should never go out and solicit business or send out a caravan or other transportation to haul you to his office and home. In my day that was considered unethical practice. The doctor wasn't seeking the patient. That's the way the practice of medicine is still supposed to be. You are supposed to pick the doctor that you like or the doctor who has been recommended. It's unethical for me to send downtown, recruit patients, haul them up to my office. We've got a couple of doctors in West Virginia who do this. They are promoting business and you aren't supposed to.

Patient Problems

Patients are intimidated by doctors. I tell my patients, "Don't be intimidated by any specialist you go to. He's just like me. You're not afraid of me. He just knows a little bit more about one thing than I do. Why should you be scared of him?" I always tell patients, "When you go to a doctor and he does a lab test on you, when he does some examination or x-ray, you tell him, 'Don't send your bill until I get the report.'" I've told them that for twenty five years because I have referred hundreds of patients who never heard a word, but they always get a bill. But nine out of ten of my patients say, "Oh, I couldn't do that." I say, "Well, if you went to the store and paid for five pounds of sugar, would you walk out because the guy wouldn't give it to you? Sugar and medicine are all the same category." You see what I mean, don't you? Why do you have the test if you're never told the results?

I don't know why people are scared of doctors. They shouldn't be. My patients aren't afraid of me. They hug me. I tell them, "You hug me now? Nobody hugged me when I was young!" Or, "You hug me, because I'm just an old man." I think some people are scared of doctors because they're scared of things that are happening in their bodies that they don't understand. And some people just don't want to know.

The other thing that worries me with patients is that patients expect the doctor to do more than the doctor can. It's hard to believe, but there are very few patients you ever see who will do things for themselves. They want it done for them. Now fifty years ago, they didn't expect you to do as much. If you told the patient, "You will have to take this medicine for ten days," they usually took it for ten days. Now if you tell them, "You need to walk a mile every day," they're too occupied with other things. They'll look at you and say, "Can't you give me a shot?" If you say, "This infection you have is serious. Take your medicine and drink a lot of liquids, because the result of a bacterial infection can be a kidney infections or pericarditis. You could get that. Take your medicine and do what I tell you. Don't work, don't over exercise, don't even walk fast to make your heart beat fast." And do you think they pay any attention to that? Most of them will say, "Well, couldn't you just give me the shot?" And "I just can't take tomorrow off." You know very well that if it's a staph or strep infection, you're not going to kill it in that time—and either one of them can kill you.

It just seems that we have reached a place in medicine where people expect a quick fix. The media has made it sound so good. In other words the ads have made it sound like it's a sheer pleasure to get sick because there are so many things that can help you. In reality there isn't a lot to help you. People come in and demand antibiotics when they should not have antibiotics. Every time you take an antibiotic, you lower your resistance to disease. Every time you get an infection, the human body has substances in it that start to build a resistance. Your first resistance is a fever, your humeral response. And your second resistance is your white blood count. Those come into play first. If you take antibiotics, you destroy the body's ability to create that immunity. Secondly, you acclimatize those germs to that antibiotic so that the next attack will wipe you out. I just won't take any unless it's absolutely necessary. People look at me and say, "You must be real healthy. You've got everything in here to take." They're surprised when I say, "I've never taken one of those. I'm afraid they'll kill me. I keep those just to give to patients!" Upjohn, the pharmaceutical company, gave each of us a packet of tablets when we graduated. There were the prettiest colors of tablets in there. That fascinated patients. When you opened that thing up, it was like opening a jewel box to patients. I never, ever took the pills out of that thing.

It's not just antibiotics that patients ask for when they don't need them. They come and ask for narcotics too. I had a couple today that had "Oh, such a bad headache," and "My knee hurts," and one of them, if she had taken 150 pounds off, her knee wouldn't hurt a bit. She was that much overweight. That patient can't recover from anything until she loses weight. That's one of the problems I have. The arthritic conditions are increasing, and weight is increasing, and nobody will do anything about it.

And the other thing is smoking. Now, you don't have too much trouble with older people, because the older ones have seen so many people die that they are convinced that it's time to quit. The younger ones, well, you might as well not even talk to them about quitting. The older ones used to say, "Well, I enjoy it and I'm not going to quit the things I enjoy." After several of their friends enjoyed themselves into their graves, then they came in wanting to know what I could do to help them quit. But the young kids with Copenhagen and cigarettes, especially the girls, you might as well not talk to them. The first thing I ask them, "Do you want to get wrinkles? Do you want your teeth to fall out?" The wrinkles got more women to quit than anything else I told them.

People are living longer now, but they're only living longer because of better nutrition. They need to take care of their bodies, seek an environment that is good, and those who want to manage their own health should do the things they think are good for them like eating healthy foods. Eat to live, not live to eat. If we can just reverse that pattern, we'd all be much better off. You and I eat too much. The human body doesn't need much. That's proven again and again. It can only be reversed when people learn self-discipline, but people just want to know if there's something in the human body that will make you do those things. I don't know what you could change in the culture that would bring about fundamental changes in the ways people eat, smoke, etcetera.

At the present rate we're going, the generation right now is not going to live as long as mine. An overweight generation can't expect to live a full life. Your body is made like a machine. For example, if you're a woman about five feet four inches tall, your genetic makeup grew you a heart that supplies a lady of about 130 to 140 pounds, maximum. If you strain that same body with one hundred eighty pounds, then by mathematics, you can calculate how much that will shorten your life. It's just that simple. Your liver, your kidney, your lungs—all of those are designed for the frame your genetic background is producing. One of my professors of medicine used a simple analogy. "How long would you expect a one-ton truck to last if you hauled three tons on it? What would the life of your truck be?" That's the way he talked about the life of people. He'd say, "You can't carry three tons on a little pickup."

Recently some specialists—cardiologists especially—say it's not your weight that shortens your life. It's your measurement over your umbilicus, your belly button. If the weight is well distributed around your body, that's one thing, but if the weight is mostly in your stomach, that's not good.

If I had another child, I would not urge him or her to go into medicine. I urged the son I had to go into medicine and he did. And he did well, because he came out in the fifties. He died in 1963 but he saw the best years of medicine. But now I'd say not to be a doctor because of what you would have to put up with.

The first thing, it would cost him about $20,000 in insurance to start practicing full time. The other thing is that every agency that you submit a bill to will use every excuse they can to find somewhere where you made an error in answering one of the questions. You need to have someone who can submit your bills and never make a mistake. There are huge forms that you have to fill in and you have to code everything - all of your diseases and treatments. If there's one minor error, they'll return it all to you.

You have trouble collecting enough money. Your cash flow is always in danger unless you have a whole bunch of private individual patients who pay you cash by the call. If patients like you, you can still have a whole lot of private patients who will be from school-age children to thirty or thirty five years old. After that, most of them will have insurance of some sort. But before that age, even if they have insurance, they have a pretty big deductible, like $500, so you get cash from those patients. If you're well liked in the community, you can pick up some cash that way.

If you go to a place where no one knows you, it would be difficult to start unless you take a paying job in a hospital with an emergency room. That's why there are a lot of doctors, including my stepson, who have never been anything other than an emergency room doctor. My stepson is an excellent doctor at West Florida Regional Medical Center and he doesn't have any relationship with his patients at all. He's always been in the emergency room and never in family practice. Emergency room doctors have time off and they are paid pretty well, if they're good. Emergency room doctors are paid well because Medicare still allows hospitals to charge one hundred to one hundred fifty dollars for a visit to the emergency room. They certainly pay as much as $100,000 a year at the Pocahontas Memorial Hospital for an emergency room doctor.

Your Medicare patients say, "Well, if you can't see me tonight, I'll just go to the emergency room." Emergency rooms love Medicare patients because that's the only place in the hospital where they make money. If you look at your Medicare or insurance bill that comes out of the emergency room, it'll be three hundred to five hundred dollars. They itemize everything they do. It'll be 125 dollars for the emergency room visit itself. My wife goes to a gynecologist. She went for her annual visit. The hospital charged two hundred twenty two dollars for the room, and his fee was only eighty seven dollars. If he had been out in private practice somewhere, I bet he could have certainly maintained a room for two hundred twenty two. But all in all, her visit was something like four hundred fifty dollars, and only eighty seven of that was his personal fee.

Either the patient has to rebel or the doctors just have to quit taking it. I have said time and again that if I was just coming out as a new doctor, I would have no staff privileges at any hospital. I would set up my own office. I would put out a sign on the outside, "I accept private patients only. My fee is ten dollars." And I think I could make it. I think enough patients would spend ten dollars for a doctor who sits down, takes his time, and talks to them. Many patients would come and pay that before they would go through the hassle of paying astronomical costs for simple health insurance and fooling around with all of the required paperwork.

And something like that may eventually happen. I think I could do that and set the fee at a maximum of twenty dollars and make money. If I was still in Green Bank and I saw twenty patients, I'd be in good shape. I could take my time with them, talk to them all day long. I could start at eight in the morning, and stay until six in the evening. Come home for supper. Feel

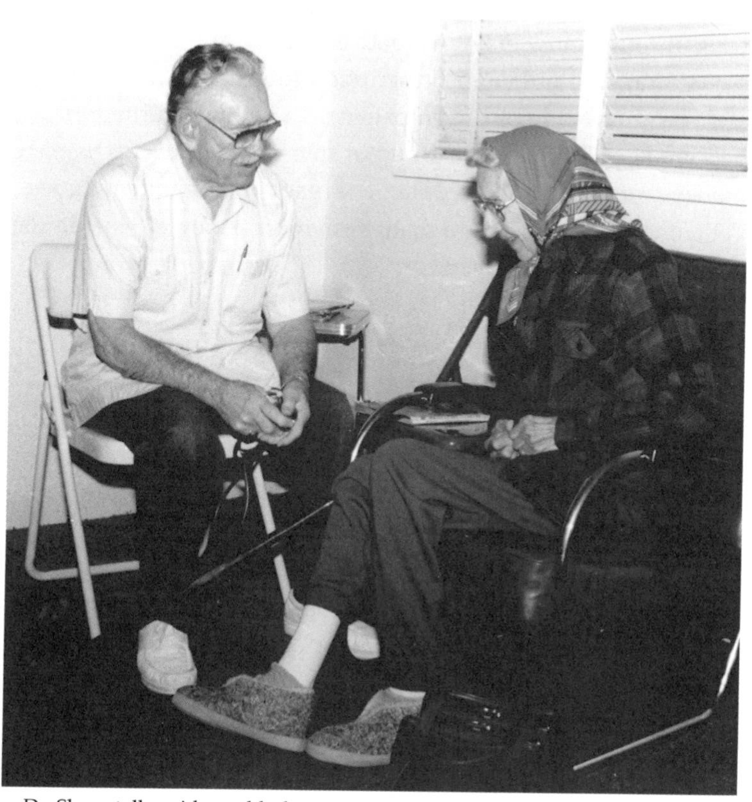

Dr. Sharp talks with an elderly patient in his Green Bank clinic waiting room.

like I'd done a decent day's work. And feel like I'd been of some benefit to the patient.

Now, if you belong to a Health Maintenance Organization, [HMO] some of those doctors take plenty of time, but those are the really conscientious ones. Pretty soon, though, they lose their job or they move somewhere else. The HMO makes money on doctors who can see patients quickly. If those doctors can walk through and make a good educated guess of what the patient has, write them a prescription to get them out of there, and see an average of fifteen patients an hour, then the HMO is happy. The HMO is just a group of shysters that sets up to make money, not to serve the people. That's why I'm so bitter, I guess. Patients just don't seem to matter anymore—they are lost in the bureaucracy and the greed.

TRIBUTES

Mentor, Philanthropist, Toucher of Lives

Olen Jones, Ph.D.
President, West Virginia School of Osteopathic Medicine

It's not often I'm asked to reflect on the life of someone like Dr. Roland Sharp. It is indeed my pleasure. What an incredible life he has led. From his humble beginnings growing up on a farm in Frost, WV, he became a grade school teacher and later made his way to the osteopathic medical school in Kirksville, Missouri. At the time he knew nothing about the osteopathic profession, but he was impressed and intrigued by medicine and began to teach classes and also attend medical school at the same time. What unbelievable perseverance! After almost two decades practicing medicine in the coal fields of West Virginia, he moved back to Green Bank in 1962 and continued an illustrious career as a rural primary care doctor—a career that has flourished ever since.

It's one thing to have a vision. It's quite another to put up your own money to see that vision become a reality. But that's exactly what Dr. Sharp did in the early seventies when he was approached with an idea to purchase a historic military school in Lewisburg, WV and turn it into an osteopathic medical school. He not only helped purchase the current school property, but the Board of Trustees later voted him president of the fledgling school, even though he hadn't really thrown his hat in the ring!

During the four years he served as president of WVSOM, Dr. Sharp was a wonderful administrator and a capable leader. But he missed practicing medicine. By 1978 he was ready to head back to his little office in Green Bank and get back to doing what he does best—helping people.

It's certainly not a stretch to say that Roland Sharp has been one of WVSOM's staunchest supporters over the years. His road to becoming an osteopathic physician was indeed a long and arduous one, and it seems to have created in him an appreciation and love for the profession that is evident in both his moral support and his philanthropy.

When it came time to name our alumni center, I couldn't think of anyone more fitting than Dr. Roland Sharp. He has mentored so many of our students, touched so many lives, and pledged unwavering support for our institution. He is a fixture at all of our school events and ceremonies.

Roland, I'd like to wish you and your family well. Most of all I'd like to thank you for your dedication to osteopathic medicine, osteopathic medical education, and the community.

Lewisburg, West Virginia
September 2007

A Caring and Commanding Presence

John Sharp, Ph.D., D.O.
Family Practitioner

I had heard of my cousin Dr. Roland Sharp for years. He was a first cousin through my grandmother and his mother [sisters] and a second cousin through his father and my grandfather [first cousins], and we had met at family gatherings and elsewhere. He is thirty-three years older than I and did not live in Pocahontas County when I was growing up, and therefore he did not have much of an influence on my early life.

Sometime in 1973 I received a phone call from Dr. Sharp. I was a Ph.D. research chemist at the Upjohn Company in Kalamazoo, Michigan. He asked if I would be interested in coming back to West Virginia to help start an osteopathic medical school in Lewisburg and help teach biochemistry. First, I did not know what an osteopath was, and second, I was an organic chemist, not a biochemist. But life is a challenge and Dr. Roland P. Sharp just became my mentor. Thirty years later Dr. Roland is turning 100 years old. I am a practicing osteopathic physician in Dr. Roland's former office in Green Bank, WV; and WVSOM is accepting two hundred students in its freshman class. It has been ranked in the top fifty medical schools by *U.S. News & World Report* for the past ten years or so, and many years in the top ten.

Dr. Sharp is a genuine, humble, honest, kind, and caring person and physician. Time is not important because he has time for everyone. The most amazing characteristic of Dr. Sharp is the combination of his memory, his mind, and his intellect and vision. His presence commands respect, and thus he was able to get the Greenbrier College of Osteopathic Medicine [currently West Virginia School of Osteopathic Medicine], up and running. The rest is history.

My first professional meeting with Dr. Sharp was when I came to Lewisburg to discuss the vision and the plan of the osteopathic medical school with Dr. Sharp, Fred Smith, Dr. Joe Rogers, D.O., Sue Keller, Betty Blatt, Ph.D, Pat Bentley, Ph.D. and D.O., Dr. Nadir Khan, M.D., and Dr. Jerry Bailes, D.O. It was amazing to observe Dr. Sharp, a country family practice physician from Pocahontas County, West Virginia, heading up and being president of the college—coordinating the synergistic energies and talents of this diverse group to produce WVSOM as it is today.

For the first few months most of us had "rooms" in the old Greenbrier Military School dorms in Lewisburg. One corner "suite" had a kitchenette where we would gather for breakfast. Dr. Roland would fix up bacon, eggs, and toast with butter. I commented that all that grease was unhealthy, but Dr. Roland told me, "It was not in our genes, so don't worry—eat up!" As he turns one hundred years old, I hope our genetics hold true.

Teaching at the college was no problem, despite a lack of equipment and supplies. Dr. Roland had taught in one- and two-room schools in Pocahontas County, so he provided all of us with a little room with small Greenbrier Military School desks, a blackboard, chalk, and erasers. And we taught the basic sciences of medicine. Some days we had to buy our own chalk and dust our own erasers. Dr. Roland also taught histology. The basic sciences were not taught in the traditional manner. Dr. Rogers and Dr. Sharp and the others had designed a coordinated, integrated system of teaching in which all the basic science disciplines—biochemistry, histology, anatomy, pharmacology, microbiology, physiology, and even clinical diagnosis—were present at each lecture.

"The proof of the pudding is in the eating," and the Greenbrier College of Osteopathic Medicine grew to become the West Virginia School of Osteopathic Medicine and to where it is today, thanks to Drs. Roland P. Sharp, Joe Rogers, and Jerry Bailes.

Today, Dr. Roland P. Sharp's memory is still as sharp as ever. It's still amazing! He cooks and eats greasy bacon and eggs. He still drives all over. He still actively farms, goes to professional continuing medical education meetings, and cares for his wife. He reads medical journals and discusses medicine, and patients still come by his house for advice and treatment. And he never says no!

Green Bank, West Virginia
September 2007

A Life Writ Large

Paula Sharp Jones
Granddaughter

My grandfather has lived a life that is extraordinary by any measure. His amazing longevity is more than matched by the rich, robust tapestry of his experiences, woven steadfastly across 100 years in these West Virginia mountains. His life story is in fact an epic yarn, a chronicle of life during a century that has seen unprecedented changes. In these pages, my grandfather spins that yarn in his own words—authentic, compelling words that are elegant in their simplicity. While this is the story of his personal journey, it is also a remarkable oral history of rural medicine in the Twentieth Century. Most importantly, the entire work is imbued with what I will call "wisdom from the big chair." He is enjoying the gifts of clarity and perspective that only a life writ large can grant.

My grandfather always seemed larger than life to me, even long before he approached the ranks of centenarians. He was loved and revered in the community. It seemed as if everyone in Pocahontas County and its environs knew "Doc Sharp." As a child, I decided that he must be the American equivalent of royalty. He was and is a gifted physician, a scholar, a philanthropist, a gentleman farmer, and a devoted patriarch for our family. Even as he nears 100, his work ethic remains utterly amazing.

Never were those proverbial "larger than life" achievements or that ethic more visible to me than when I helped edit the pages of this manuscript. Frequently, I would get lost in the compelling, often humorous, and sometimes harrowing accounts of his exploits as a physician. The whole tale of the